A bridge to the future

Profitable construction for tomorrow's industry and it customers

Roger Flanagan

Ian Ingram

Laurence Marsh

 Thomas Telford RCF

Published by Thomas Telford Publishing, Thomas Telford Ltd,
1 Heron Quay, London E14 4JD.

URL: http://www.t-telford.co.uk

The research reported in this document was funded by
EPSRC Innovative Manufacturing Initiative
Reading Construction Forum

PO Box 219, Whiteknights, Reading RG6 6AW.

Distributors for Thomas Telford books are

USA: ASCE Press, 1801 Alexander Bell Drive, Reston, VA 20191-4400, USA

Japan: Maruzen Co. Ltd, Book Department, 3–10 Nihonbashi 2-chome, Chuo-ku, Tokyo 103

Australia: DA Books and Journals, 648 Whitehorse Road, Mitcham 3132, Victoria

First published 1998

Also from Reading Construction Forum available from Thomas Telford Books

Seven Pillars of Partnering

Trusting the Team

A catalogue record for this book is available from the British Library

ISBN: 0 7277 2714 1

Design and layout by Kneath Associates Limited, Swansea

Printed and bound in Great Britain by Thanet Press Ltd, Margate

Contents

Forewords 2

Acknowledgements 4

A bridge to the future 5

Executive summary 7

1. Where are we now and how did we get here? 11

Pen picture of the construction industry today 11

Looking back 13

The present - where is the industry today? 15

Change in the business environment 15

2. Where do we want to go? 21

The importance of the customer 21

How can we do better? 25

Achieving the vision 29

3. Improving product delivery 31

Supply chain management 32

Lean principles in construction 34

4. Using technology for process improvement 41

Enabling technologies 42

Enabling technologies in the lean supply chain 47

Electronic commerce in construction 49

Using enabling technologies in operation and maintenance 50

Trends in the UK construction supply chain - results of a survey 50

Some of the real life barriers to innovation 51

Partnering/technology partnerships 52

5. Shaping people and tomorrow's construction organizations 55

The challenges 55

Tomorrow's construction organization 57

People issues within technological and process change 60

Meeting the demands of tomorrow 61

6. The next stage 63

Preparing for the future: steps to change 63

Four steps to achieving lean design 63

Three steps to achieving lean supply 64

Project 2010: A vision of construction in the year 2010 66

Bibliography and references 67

The Reading Construction Forum 69

Forewords

John Anderson

Managing Director

Bovis Europe

I passionately believe in the necessity and desirability of major change and improvement in our industry. This report, put together by the Reading Construction Forum Task Force and by Professor Roger Flanagan and his research team, looks at the steps needed to improve the processes within the industry using available technology.

Our future success will depend on our people, our products and the processes we use. People are the industry's knowledge base, they conceive and produce the product and manage the process. Our processes are not yet world best and we must work hard to embrace the philosophy of a non-adversarial approach and the change of culture this involves. We have the technology, we just need to make use of it. It is not an easy goal to strive for but it is a worthwhile one.

The Reading Construction Forum Task Force Team and the researchers have worked hard and well together. I would like to give my sincere thanks to Keith Roberts of ROM, Alan Baker of Gleeds and Nigel Woolcock of the Prudential Portfolio Managers for their contributions to this work based on their wide-ranging experience of the industry. My thanks also to Professor Roger Flanagan and his team for their enormous contribution and for their tolerance and persistence in bringing this project to a successful completion.

There is nothing new under the sun, but I hope this report will help to bridge the gap between today's reality and tomorrow's vision.

The construction industry has changed more over the last ten years than it has over the last fifty. It is changing for the better. This welcome trend needs to continue and, above all, to extend beyond our first division players to the rest of the industry. Technology has played a key role in this dramatic change, yet in some areas we still use construction methods and processes that date back hundreds of years; building with bricks and mortar is an example. The industry will not totally transform itself overnight, nor should it seek to. It has strengths and weaknesses and, with that, threats and opportunities. The industry needs to build on its strengths, not just by the improvement of the large construction organizations that have plenty of resources but by the many small and medium organizations that have an equally major impact on the industry as a whole. The re-engineering of the basic processes that are used by all firms, irrespective of size and type of work, and a change in mind-set from confrontation to teamwork, have a major role to play in building a successful and prosperous industry. Some key issues need to be addressed by the industry and its clients:

Sir John Egan

Chairman of the Construction Task Force

Chief Executive, BAA plc

- The enlightened customer is driving change. The industry needs to respond by focusing on the needs of their customers and their customer's customer.

- The supply chain is becoming more complex and its key players need to become integrated into the project team as equal partners.

- There needs to be a widening of focus from project to process and product through lean design and lean supply.

- Technology has the potential to become an important enabler in the transformation of the business environment as a powerful and cost-effective tool for putting valuable changes into effect.

The Reading Construction Forum has commissioned and steered a number of reports which cover many important aspects of construction. These reports have been milestones in the industry's progress towards providing better value for money through becoming less adversarial and less fragmented. This report provides a vision of construction in 2010. What makes this vision achievable is that the steps to change are manageable for all sizes of company engaged in all kinds of work. They are steps that have already been taken by other industries.

I do hope that you will read this report and develop specific ideas which you feel are relevant to your organization, and use them to build your own list of practical steps and deadlines for change.

The Construction Task Force invited the reader to "Rethink construction". This report invites you to make the first move.

Acknowledgements

The authors gratefully acknowledge the valuable input provided by members of the research team - in particular Carol Jewell, Jane Fear, Dianne McGlynn and Julian Day.

The authors acknowledge the input of the members of the Reading Construction Forum and in particular the Project Task Force which consisted of:

John Anderson (Chairman)	*Bovis Europe*
Alan Baker	*Gleeds*
Keith Roberts	*ROM Ltd*
Nigel Woolcock	*Prudential Portfolio Managers Ltd*

We are grateful to the following for the supply and use of photographs within this report:

Advanced Construction Technology - The University of Reading

Bovis Europe

Building Design Partnership

Future Systems

Ove Arup & Partners

A bridge to the future
Profitable construction for tomorrow's industry and its customers

Where are we now and how did we get there? - Chapter 1

"*In no other important industry is the responsibility for design so far removed from the responsibility for production*" Sir Harold Emmerson, 1962

Nearly forty years on, little has changed. This report focuses on change and tells how the UK construction industry has become what it is today, moving from a public-sector dominated industry to one that is building a future dominated by the private sector. Customers' demands for certainty, speed of delivery, management of risk and value for money are being met by the best in the industry, the rest are being left behind. The gap between the best and the rest is widening.

Where do we want to go? - Chapter 2

Nine major industry reports over the past fifty years, from the Simon Report in 1944 to the Latham Review in 1994, have analysed the industry and identified many opportunities but, until Latham, with very little change. The difference today is the speed of change; technology is changing markets and revolutionizing communication systems. There needs to be a greater customer focus to provide what the customer wants rather than what the industry thinks the customer needs. What they want is certainty and no surprises. Sixty percent of respondents in our customer survey expressed general satisfaction with the level of value for money provided by the construction industry. A majority of respondents did not believe that contractors fully understood their customers' business needs.

How do we get there? - Chapters 3 and 4

Improving product delivery means meeting the needs of the customer, the shareholders and the global marketplace. This report advocates a more effective process which involves management of the supply chain and closer integration with the design process. A greater certainty of design, cost and time prior to starting work on site is vital. Integrating suppliers into the process and involving them before the concept design stage will significantly help to improve the process and the product.

Elimination of non-value adding activities will produce the greatest potential for improving product delivery.

Technology is a powerful tool with the potential to significantly improve the process and the product. Knowledge is information put to productive use. Technology can transform vast amounts of data into knowledge in a way that was previously impossible. Small organizations can exploit IT in order to achieve what was once only within the reach of large companies.

"*Technology on its own cannot provide the answer to the need for greater efficiency and quality in construction ... first sort out the culture, then define and improve the processes and finally apply technology as a tool.*"

'Rethinking Construction' - a report of the Construction Task Force (1998)

Shaping people and tomorrow's organization - Chapter 5

Today's organization needs to identify and implement changes to meet the demands of tomorrow's global competition. People and relationships are the key to sustainable success with greater emphasis placed on the customer, the improvement of product delivery, more transparency between design and production and better use of technology. Tomorrow's successful company will have bridged the gaps between the players and the process with a holistic approach. Money will be diverted from defensive behaviour and contractual disputes to involvement in success factors such as training, continuous improvement, and research and development. The only sustainable competitive advantage is the ability to learn faster and embrace change faster than our competitors.

CD supplement

The CD-ROM that accompanies this report is not a duplicate of the text. It provides supplementary information to give the reader a wider perspective of the work undertaken.

Executive summary

The only sustainable competitive advantage is the ability to learn faster and embrace change faster than our competitors.

The UK design and construction industry at its best is excellent - it is world class. However, increasing globalization enabled by the free flow of finance, services and products across national boundaries is creating new competitive challenges. One of the characteristics of this changing environment is the growing expectation of the industry's customers. Currently, the rate of change is outpacing the rate at which industry is improving its performance. The widening gap between expectation and delivery is at the heart of the challenge which the industry faces. Without change, the gap between what the customer expects and what the industry can offer will grow.

The gap must be closed - this report identifies opportunities and suggests an agenda for action. Change is normally seen as a threat and very difficult to initiate and manage effectively. 'Quick fixes' are elusive and frequently mistrusted. Change requires a commitment from the industry and its people. Commitment can only grow from understanding the real benefits to be gained from changing the way we do things now.

No miracle cures are on offer. We cannot change overnight the culture of the whole industry, and real action is needed.

Many reports focus upon the major players and the large, headline-grabbing, construction projects, but the vast majority of projects and firms are small to medium-sized. We are aware that many firms undertake smaller new build projects, repair and refurbishment work, usually within a limited geographical area. They are often dealing with inexperienced customers, who find it difficult to assess value-for-money and to manage the consultation process. Firms strive to keep costs down, partly driven by the tendering system, but lack time to step back and explore latest developments and their implications for businesses. You don't have to be big to be innovative or to deal with change. Small and medium-sized firms often have the advantage of being less hide-bound by tradition and being more flexible; they have less corporate baggage. The improvements offered within this report are available to all.

How the industry has been shaped

The industry has been shaped by the needs of the public sector, which was responsible for the majority of the workload. Procedures have been designed to ensure accountability and value-for-money. Contracts have been based on conflict and liability - the foundation of the 'blame culture.' Design has traditionally been separated from production by class and training, the designer was a professional while the producer was a tradesman.

All the previous major reports on the industry since 1944 have described the symptoms of a dysfunctional industry. Problems identified over half a century ago still remain. One of the strengths of the UK system of design and delivery is the flexibility to make changes after construction has commenced - this is also the weakness.

Customer focus

We need to develop a customer-focused industry that knows what its customers expect and how to improve the service offered. We need to focus on our customer's customer. Customers today are not always looking for a bargain (although they are happy when one comes along),

The future used to be relatively predictable. However, as Paul Valery said, "The trouble with our time is that the future is not what it used to be".

Most of the problems in construction are at the joins - between design and production, between components, and between contractor and specialist contractor.

Our perception is that too much money is being spent on the settlement of contractual disputes, whereas that money could be spent on investing in training and research and development.

instead they want a building that as well as offering value-for-money fulfils their cost, time, and performance requirements. Above all, they want certainty and no surprises.

The breadth of the customer base has increased and customers are very different to what they were twenty years ago, particularly with the shift of dominance from public to private-sector customers. However, customers still care more about the product than the process; they have to suffer the process to get the product.

Our customer satisfaction survey showed that 60% of customers felt the industry was responding and listening to their needs. The survey reflected the priorities of the customer, which were not necessarily the priorities of the industry.

Design and production

The traditional design-bid-build approach for larger projects is beginning to be superceded by new methods of project procurement and financing. The private finance initiative (PFI) and public/private partnerships mean that whole-life costs are now fundamentally important in determining performance criteria.

Design and production have to be seen as a seamless integrated transparent process. As the process changes, the roles and relationships across the supply chain will evolve new ways of working and new freedoms drawing on the experiences of other industries - particularly enabled by technology.

The project team with the customer should ensure that whatever procurement process is adopted, project design information should be 90% complete before starting the production phase and committing people to a price. Other industries would not start production without full information. One way this will be achieved is by the use of technology which enables people to share information.

The industry must tackle the problem of waste, not just the wastage of materials on site but the waste of time and human resources caused by any re-design and re-work of project details and inefficient processes.

Logistics and supply chain management have transformed the retail and automotive sectors. The construction industry often sees this as nothing more than common sense or management of materials. This is not the case; the construction industry will need to embrace formal logistic procedures that involve suppliers and manufacturers at an early stage in order to achieve improved profitability.

Customization of standard design details must become normal practice, using off-the-shelf components or prefabricated units leads to faster design, faster construction, lower costs, zero defects and increased certainty.

Technology

A clear and consistent message from the Technology Foresight Programme was the need for integration between design and production and the creation of a culture based on innovation. The construction industry has still to realize the benefits of the Technology Foresight Reports.

Design that embraces customized solutions using standardized components can now become a reality with the widespread use of CAD allowing early consideration of issues such as manufacturability, maintainability and whole-life appraisal with due regard for system performance. All these issues have been successfully implemented by the automotive and aerospace industries.

Developments in intelligent computer aided design (ICAD), knowledge-based engineering (KBE) and object modelling (OM) now offer the ability to integrate design, manufacture and installation more closely than ever before. The underlying reason behind this is to improve profitability. IT is a powerful tool that allows smaller organizations to achieve what was only possible by larger ones. Inevitably, the development of this technology for construction is being led by the major players. However, one characteristic of IT is the speed at which prices fall, allowing it to cascade down the value chain and provide value-for-money. Applications of the technology include early visualization for the customer, rapid design prototyping and more effective information exchange between project participants.

Electronic commerce can enable logistics and supply chain management to become an integral part of a construction organization's management. It already happens at the initial stages of projects, where large builders' merchants and suppliers use an electronic supply chain system. There needs to be no difference between the distribution of a parcel, on time to anywhere in the world, and the supply of building materials just-in-time to a site.

Specialist and trade contractors, component manufacturers and builders' merchants, whatever their size of turnover, form a major part of the supply chain. Technical input from specialist contractors at the concept design stage allows the design team more freedom to expand the knowledge base and extend the boundaries of what can be achieved.

Construction sites are swamped in paper, much of the paper is difficult to trace and retrieve, much of the paper is simply written to defend somebody's contractual position. Meanwhile, technologies such as auto-ID (automatic identification) can yield radical improvements in managing and providing such information.

Just as information has superseded data, knowledge will soon supersede information. Businesses are becoming knowledge-based by putting information to productive use. Importantly, knowledge will be incorporated within construction products to communicate information to the consumer in a practical way.

People and organizations

Yesterday's company sees customers as a source of profit and competes only on price. Tomorrow's company seeks to add value for customers. Yesterday's company had adversarial attitudes towards trading partners. Tomorrow's company sees employees, customers, suppliers and investors as stakeholders. Only by deepening stakeholder relationships can tomorrow's company anticipate, innovate and adapt fast enough. Tomorrow's company sees key suppliers as an extension of the company. It sets joint targets and shares information and ideas.

Construction organizations will have to change. Experts suggest that the future will be characterized by a small number of mega players, increased specialization, greater emphasis on non-price factors in tendering, flatter and leaner management structures and seamless electronic integration between firms.

People and relationships are the keys to sustainable success. Technical and process improvements imply change to working patterns and challenge existing attitudes. Successful implementation of this report's recommendations will depend critically on effective communication, education, training, participation and involvement. The successful construction organization consists of people who are flexible and responsive to external forces and circumstances. To attain this, firms need to build on people's abilities, rather than limiting them for the convenience of easily recognized roles.

Moving forward

The industry needs practical examples of other people's success before advances will be more widely embraced. Some customers are already undertaking demonstration projects to test their ideas. More are planned as advocated in the report of the Construction Task Force (1998).

The Reading Construction Forum steering group for this project looked at what changes would be happening to a construction project by 2010. Many of the perceived changes are already happening in the best leading-edge companies. The Reading Construction Forum therefore supports the initiative that demonstration projects be set up to utilize the Project 2010 objectives.

Bridging the gaps

- There is a gap between what the customer wants and what the current industry's process provides.
- There is a gap between the best in the industry and the average.
- There is a gap in the take-up of technology by different parts of the industry. There is a gap between performance and speed of change in other industries compared with the construction sector. Construction has not improved as fast as manufacturing, aerospace or the oil and gas industry.
- There is a gap between what the head office's view of what should happen on site and what is actually happening.
- There is a gap between the skills available and the skills needed in a modern construction industry.

The key to the future lies with developing the people, improving the process and creating value in the product which is achieved by:

- Having greater *customer focus*.
- Making *design and production* a seamless process.
- Using *technology* to improve the design and construction process and the product.
- Developing *people and shaping organizations* to cope with change effectively.

Chapter 1
Where are we now and how did we get here?

Pen picture of the construction industry today

Construction is a global industry, with a total annual output of around US$3 trillion. The three major construction markets in the world are the USA, Europe and Japan (Figure 1). Despite its size, the UK is seen as one of the leading players in the industry and with world-wide influence. Britain has been very innovative in bringing about change in the industry - a prime example is the shift from public to private-sector finance for infrastructure investments. The breakdown of the type of work in the UK industry, when compared with most other European countries, shows a high proportion of repair and maintenance work, a strong dependence on the private sector and a relatively low spend on new infrastructure (Figures 2 and 3). Figure 4 shows the UK output compared with some European countries. The output for Germany includes infrastructure and building work following unification. Furthermore, some countries account for the black economy in construction work in the output figures.

Fantasy	Fact
■ The project design is almost complete prior to work starting on site.	■ Most projects are only 50% design complete prior to work starting on site.
■ Trust prevails between all the parties.	■ There is a lack of trust, with nobody trusting anybody.
■ Information technology has revolutionized construction.	■ CAD systems are now commonplace. Only larger firms have any facility to trade electronically. The impact of IT is only just starting.
■ Contract procedures and contracts have become more streamlined.	■ Sites are swamped with paper because everybody wants to protect their contractual position.
■ Specialist contractors and suppliers are involved at the design stage.	■ Only on some major projects and in a few enlightened cases do the specialists get involved at the design stage.
■ Construction workers in many overseas countries work longer and harder than UK site operatives.	■ Construction workers in the UK are as productive as anywhere in the world given the same conditions and equipment. It is the process and its management that causes the problem, with too much flexibility in the system.
■ Everybody is in favour of higher profit margins to pay for investment in research and development.	■ Profit margins for construction work are low around the world. Improvements in profit will need to come from improvements in efficiency.

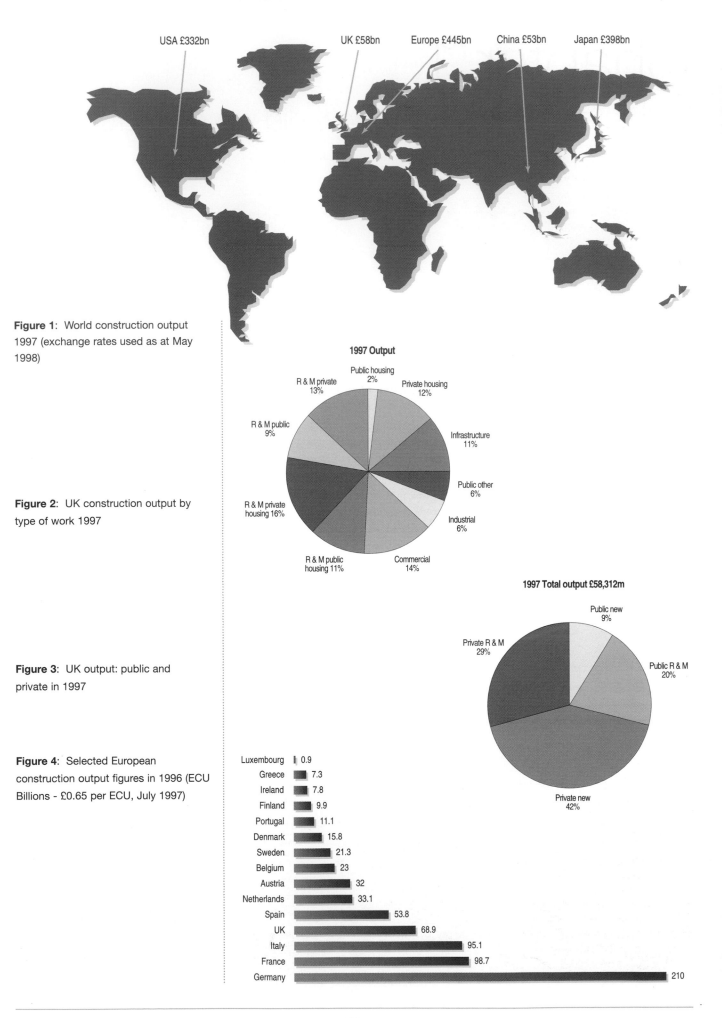

USA £332bn UK £58bn Europe £445bn China £53bn Japan £398bn

Figure 1: World construction output 1997 (exchange rates used as at May 1998)

1997 Output

Public housing 2%
Private housing 12%
R & M private 13%
R & M public 9%
Infrastructure 11%
Public other 6%
R & M private housing 16%
Industrial 6%
R & M public housing 11%
Commercial 14%

Figure 2: UK construction output by type of work 1997

1997 Total output £58,312m

Public new 9%
Private R & M 29%
Public R & M 20%
Private new 42%

Figure 3: UK output: public and private in 1997

Figure 4: Selected European construction output figures in 1996 (ECU Billions - £0.65 per ECU, July 1997)

Luxembourg	0.9
Greece	7.3
Ireland	7.8
Finland	9.9
Portugal	11.1
Denmark	15.8
Sweden	21.3
Belgium	23
Austria	32
Netherlands	33.1
Spain	53.8
UK	68.9
Italy	95.1
France	98.7
Germany	210

Looking back

Two things are especially striking about the past 800 years of building history. The first is that at no time has there been widespread use of a single or a standard method for procuring buildings; time and again people have tried new ways as a result of their dissatisfaction with previous methods. The second is how little the problems have changed over the years, and how regularly the same ones crop up. In 1256 Henry III complained he had "suffered much [financial] damage" at the hands of builders. It is clear from many historical records that from at least the time of Henry III the quest for most people who have commissioned a building has been to get a clear idea, before construction starts, of what the building will be like, when it will be completed, how much it will cost and whether it will represent good value-for-money.

Key lessons from the past

Reviewing the history of the construction industry reveals some important observations, pointing to how the industry has developed into its present form.

- Design teams offered unbiased professional advice and services and worked for the customer for a fixed fee while contractors won work by bidding the lowest tender (which included overheads and profit).

- Contract awards were usually based on the lowest bid for construction using competitive tendering. Quality of service was a by-product.

- Barriers to entry into the industry were low, with no requirements for tradespeople, builders, engineers or surveyors to be registered or regulated.

- Design was seen as a separate process from construction. Design and build was commonly seen as a solution that provided buildings that lack innovation and inspiration in design.

- CAD technology speeded up the design production process, but design and production were still separate processes carried out under different contracts.

- Specialist contracting and labour-only subcontracting increasingly replaced a lot of direct employment. Nobody talked about the supply chain.

- Contractual positions had to be protected, resulting in contracts being more and more complex as they sought to close 'loopholes'.

- The design sequence followed the *RIBA Plan of Work*, developed in the mid-1960s.

- Nomination was an early form of partnering - it went because of contractual issues.

Standardization seemed to have worked in 1851, why not in 1998?

The Crystal Palace, London - 1851. Designed by Joseph Paxton, built by Fox Henderson & Co. Price agreed £79,800 to erect and dismantle the structure. Final account for erection £200,000. Contract duration - 20 weeks. Finished on time. Floor area 750,000 sq ft. Steelwork 4,500 tons. Standardized units, off-site fabrication based on a 24 ft bay. Crystal Palace brought about a new debate regarding the effect of industrialization on design

Figure 5: Opportunities identified in previous industry reports

	Simon 1944	Emms'n 1956	Emms'n 1962	Tavistock 1963	Banwell 1964	Tavistock 1966	NEDO 1967	BPF 1983	Latham 1994
Technology									
New material development									
Increased technical complexity									
New process									
Organization									
Outstripped by technology developments									
Adherence too outmoded procedures									
Development of subcontracting/specialists									
Interdependence of activities									
Division of responsibility									
Uncertainty									
People									
Relationships/cooperation									
Integration of design and construction									
Partnering									
Efficiency									
Low productivity and poor return									
Standardization									
Construction as a manufacturing process									
Prefabrication and modularization									
Mechanization									
Pre construction									
Role of the building owner									
Public-sector emphasis									
Private-sector emphasis									
Fragmented customer base									
Effective briefing									
Effective planning and coordination									
Management of design									
Competitive tendering									
Criticism of competitive tendering – outmoded									
Lack of final and detailed information									
Questioning of value of B of Q									
Reduction of subsequent changes									
Selective tendering									
Burdensome qualification procedures									
Negotiation									
Serial contracting									
Site management									
Lack of information									
Training									
Coordination role									
Division of responsibility									
Benefit of early contractor input									
Reduction of changes									
Adoption of incentives									
Legal/contractual									
Increased litigation/arbitration									
Increased claims and variations									
Prompt agreement – claims and variations									
Payment									
Prompt and regular payment									
Elimination of retention money									
Rethinking of fee structure									
Revamp of payment procedures									

■ The government and public-sector customers played a major role in shaping the industry; they were the dominant customers and most of the procedures were shaped to meet public-sector requirements.

A good measure of the past is to examine nine major reports, ranging from the 1944 Simon Report to the 1994 Latham Review, that have reviewed the performance, procedures, practices and problems of the construction industry over the past 50 years. Their analysis helps to produce an understanding of how the industry has been shaped the way it has. Figure 5 shows the opportunities for the industry that were identified in each of the successive reviews. It is a salutary message, but very little fundamental or radical change has taken place in either the product or the process, despite the good intentions. However, the Latham Review has started to reverse this trend - some of its recommendations are now on the statute books, while others are actively being pursued. It is significant that profitability within the industry was not addressed, and that the industry continues to operate at very low margins.

The nature of the industry's workload has changed significantly over the past 40 years, shifting away from the public accountability required when the industry was

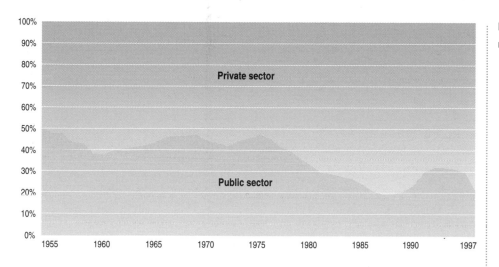

dominated by public-sector work, to the demands for certainty, speed of delivery,
management of risk and value-for-money by the now dominant private sector
(Figure 6). The industry's performance has notably improved over the past decade.

The present - where is the industry today?

As with lessons from the past, the state of the construction industry today can be
summarized by a few key observations.

- Change is constant. Change in the construction industry is influenced by a
large number of factors, including interest rates, business uncertainty,
government policy, European and world events, training and the changing
expectations of customers. Everyone agrees the industry must respond to the
customer's demands instead of continuing to offer the traditional approach.

- A gap is opening between organizations best prepared to meet the challenges
ahead and those organizations structured for the 1980s' model of the industry.
The best UK designers and constructors are among the best in the world. The
best in the industry are leaving the rest behind, and the divergence is increasing.

- Innovative customers are demanding a more efficient delivery process. All
customers want lower construction costs. Britain is striving to reduce costs
by 30%, but we are not alone. Similar targets have been set in the USA,
Japan and across Europe. Partnering is being seen as one route to developing
the long-term relationships and trust necessary for efficient delivery.

- Site production processes are changing. Construction has to be treated as a
manufacturing process and must adopt a production engineering approach
using lean manufacturing for design and construction.

- Profitability in the UK industry is low. The gross profit margin for construction
organizations is around 1% of the project cost. The position is no better globally.
It is no use simply arguing that profit margins are too low, the target has to be to
increase efficiency and drive down costs to achieve better profitability.

- The industry is dysfunctional. The symptoms are the delivery of projects late and
over budget, low productivity and poor returns, and slow take-up of new technology.

Change in the business environment

The world business environment is becoming ever more complex, demanding and fast-
changing, both in speed and scope. Technology is changing markets and
revolutionizing information and communications - the fastest growing element in
world trade is information.

The product and the process

- The customers are interested in
the product and not the process,
but they recognize the importance
of the process.

- The contractor is interested in how
the process can deliver the
product.

- The specialist-contractor is
interested in his product, suffers
the process but would like to
change the process to reflect the
important role he can play - if only
somebody would ask.

- The supplier is interested in getting
his product out of the factory door
and keeping clear of the rest of the
process.

Pen Picture of the UK Construction industry

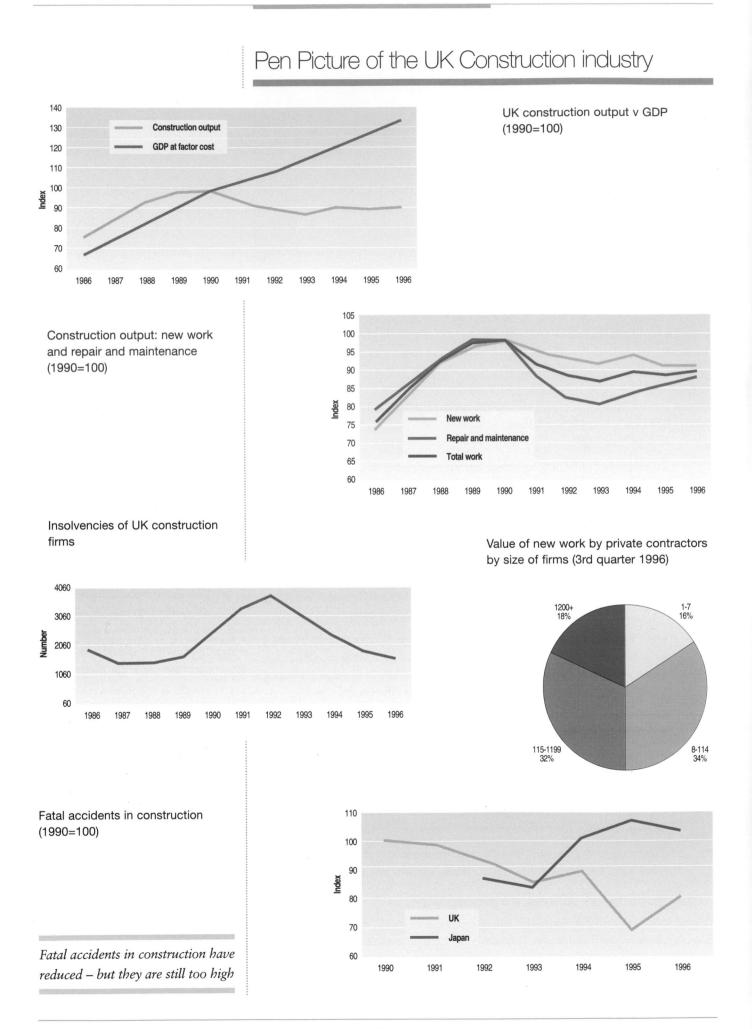

UK construction output v GDP
(1990=100)

Construction output: new work
and repair and maintenance
(1990=100)

Insolvencies of UK construction
firms

Value of new work by private contractors
by size of firms (3rd quarter 1996)

Fatal accidents in construction
(1990=100)

*Fatal accidents in construction have
reduced – but they are still too high*

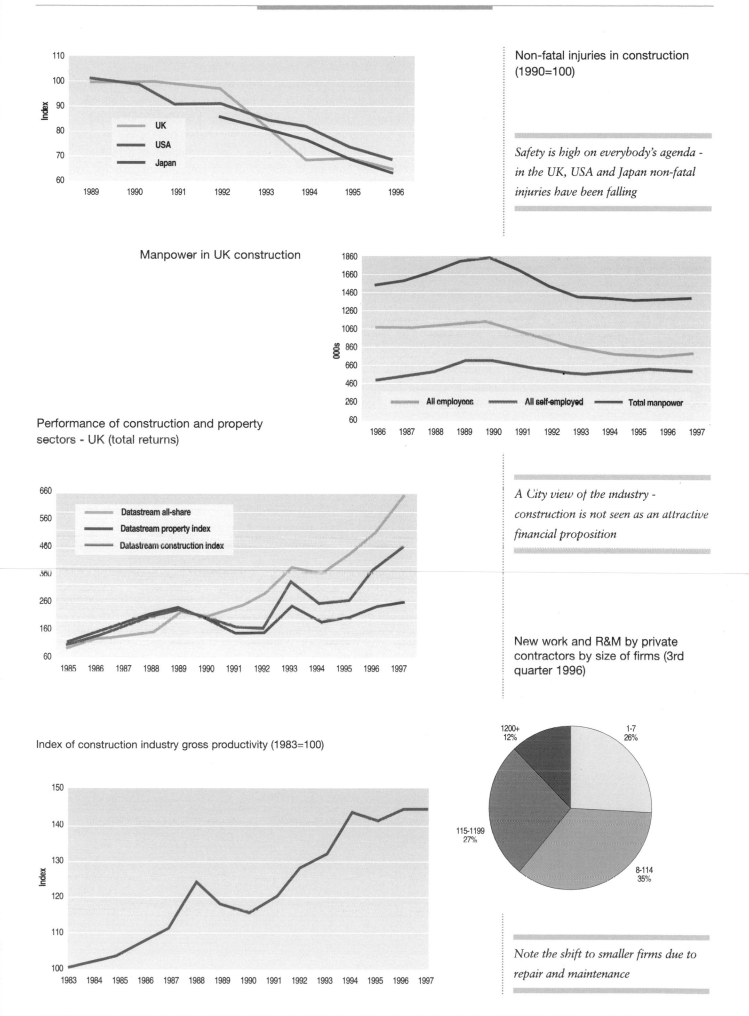

Non-fatal injuries in construction
(1990=100)

Safety is high on everybody's agenda - in the UK, USA and Japan non-fatal injuries have been falling

Manpower in UK construction

Performance of construction and property sectors - UK (total returns)

A City view of the industry - construction is not seen as an attractive financial proposition

New work and R&M by private contractors by size of firms (3rd quarter 1996)

Index of construction industry gross productivity (1983=100)

Note the shift to smaller firms due to repair and maintenance

A new process

The *RIBA Plan of Work*, devised in 1965 and perhaps the best known process model, was developed for building a £300,000 public housing scheme. This is no longer an appropriate project upon which to base the methodology for construction process management. The *Plan of Work* fails to take into account the complexities of today's industry. If the industry is to meet the demands of its customers in the 21st century then it will need to work within a different framework.

Globalization

The impact of globalization is that instead of the world being made up of a series of different economies that determine their own business conditions, the economic conditions in most parts of the world will be determined by the overall world economic position. Globalization of markets, supply chains, finance and work is creating competition on an unprecedented scale. Global competition is leading companies to develop new business strategies and new employment patterns, creating a growing number of small specialized companies and an increase in self-employment. New organizational structures are emerging, producing the networked organization which outsources services and streamlines corporate centres.

Funding

The shift from public to private-sector funding of infrastructure and public-sector facilities has led to the emergence of new types of project funding and management, such as build-operate-transfer (BOT) and the private finance initiative (PFI). These are growing in scope and importance and will change the perception of risk and the approach to managing risk for the construction sector.

International legislation on environmental issues is moving towards the 'polluter pays' principle, where the environmental impact of a project is taxed. This implies additional risks to be considered and managed.

Business success

The centre of gravity of business success is shifting from the exploitation of a company's physical assets to the realization of creativity and learning potential of its staff and people with whom it has contact. The shift is referred to as moving from the hardware of the construction industry to exploiting software skills through knowledge workers. All construction organizations need to become learning organizations.

Responding to customers

The industry must respond to customers' demands and shed the image of offering the traditional approach. It should no longer separate design from production and should ensure involvement of the suppliers and specialists at the design phase. This is reinforced by the Construction Task Force Report (1998) which advocates greater integration.

To meet customers needs, the industry needs to:

■ reduce costs, add value and sharpen international competitiveness

■ increase the amount of work that involves collaboration and industrial participation to ensure that construction adds value to customers' businesses

■ create greater collaboration between the industry and its suppliers by implementing effective supply chain management.

Some of the changes that are happening: The Housing Grants, Construction and Regeneration Act 1996

"The most significant piece of legislation to hit the industry for decades. It will fundamentally change the nature of contractual relationships."

Building 17/4/98

The act attempts to produce a regime of fairer payment and to improve cash flow within the industry. The main points are:

- a requirement of all contracts to state clearly what will be paid and when, with a ban on the use of pay-when-paid clauses
- a contract must provide for payment by instalments if the work is to take longer than 45 days, or otherwise a 28-day payment cycle
- a contract must provide an adequate mechanism for determining what sums are due and who is responsible for the valuation
- an ability for any party to suspend work if they have not been paid sums due by the final date of payment
- a statutory right to refer disputes to adjudication - a procedure must be included in the contract.

What does it mean to ...

Consultants

- Their contract of employment is covered by the Act.
- The schedule of fee payments must be checked carefully as the scheme is more applicable to construction contracts.
- They need to be covered by a professional indemnity insurance for an adjudicator's award.

Contractors

- Payment terms within their contract should be checked for compliance with the Act.
- They should identify potential adjudicators.
- Be aware of specialists' use of the Act as they can refer 20 to 30 cases a month to an adjudicator.

Specialists

- The contract needs to be in place as soon as possible as the payment cycles begin as soon as the contract is signed.
- Be aware of contractors trying to impose long payment cycles.
- Prepare standard documentation to deal with the adjudication rules, the contractor can influence the choice of adjudicator.

"I am certain that this legislation will, if used sensibly, help the industry to reduce time wasted in conflict and to focus its energies on constructing buildings and infrastructure, and providing real value for money to its customers."

Nick Raynsford, Construction Minister

Chapter 2
Where do we want to go?

The importance of the customer

The UK construction industry's customer base is more diverse today than ever before. Privatization has created many new customers and new methods of financing (e.g. syndicated loans) have increased the range of organizations involved. The problem everyone in the industry faces today is 'who is the customer?' No matter where in the supply chain a business operates, it must start thinking about its customer's customer. The organization commissioning the project is ultimately everyone's customer - without it nobody has a project to work on.

Customers get fed up hearing that:

■   the construction industry is different from other industries - it is more complex and fragmented

■   every project is unique and hence a prototype - so things go wrong

■   don't get contractors involved in the design process - they will seek to maximize profit at the expense of good design

■   the project is late because ... .

The truth is that most industries are complex, often requiring long supply chains. Industries such as aircraft manufacturing, shipbuilding and process engineering deliver major one-off capital items, frequently customized or made-to-order, however their components and materials are often sourced world-wide.

You read a book from beginning to end. You run a business the opposite way - you start at the end and then do everything you must do to reach it. In other words, don't just sit around dreaming up new products; you go to the customers, discover their choices and preferences and then deliver them as precisely as possible.

Sir Colin Marshall,
British Airways

Who is the customer?

■   The development company sees the investors, the financiers and the tenants as the customers.

■   The consultants and construction firms are clear who the customer is.

■   The specialist contractors, builders' merchants, and material and component suppliers see the construction firm as the customer.

■   The labour-only firms see the specialist contractor as the customer.

■   The site operatives see the organization paying their wages as the customer.

The Construction Clients' Forum's manifesto puts forward specific areas for change within the industry. The Forum believes that by customers and the construction industry working together, the industry can improve its overall performance by:

- presenting customers with objective and appropriate advice on the options and choices to meet their needs
- introducing a 'right first time' culture with the projects finished on time and to budget
- eliminating waste, streamlining processes and working towards continuous improvement
- working towards standardization of components where this provides efficiency gains
- using a properly trained and certified workforce and keeping skills up to date
- keeping abreast of changing technology by innovation and investment in research and development.

In other industries, technology leaders have forced change. In construction, this role has frequently fallen to the customer. Leading companies, such as Tesco, McDonald's, Stanhope, Sainsbury's and BP, have proved that projects can be built quickly and effectively by:

- having a clearly defined brief
- incorporating standard manufactured components
- using standardized design solutions
- maximizing the use of off-site pre-fabrication
- integrating the manufacturers and component suppliers into the supply chain
- using partnering.

The customers have driven the change and the industry has demonstrated it can respond to these challenges positively.

Housing: a success story

One sector of the construction industry that has changed in response to customer needs is the housing sector. Private-sector housing has become a niche market, with firms competing on the basis of value-added services to suit the needs of a developing customer base. This has been achieved by the customization of standard design solutions, the availability of finance and part-exchange deals. Branding of both the product and the provider is fundamental to success in this sector.

New types of customers

The more forward-thinking firms in design and construction are becoming specialized and are seeking niche areas. The generic 'customer' of the past no longer exists. The changes in the method and type of project financing (with the industry embracing BOT and PFI) has led to further diversification in the customer base.

What do customers want?

The construction industry is often unclear about what customers want. To overcome this construction organizations must clearly identify and align themselves with their individual customer requirements. This means finding them, listening to them, thinking like them, anticipating their needs and solving their problems. Achieving customer satisfaction has to be worked at continuously. Success depends on fully understanding the customers' business needs and then designing to meet, or ideally exceed, those needs. Once this has been achieved, the process and procedures for delivery should be

Tesco has reduced the capital cost of its stores by 40% in five years.

Whitbread Hotels has reduced construction time of its hotels by 40%.

Housing construction in Britain has been revolutionized over the past ten years by standard design and standard off-the-shelf components. The UK housing sector is highly regarded overseas.

retained and reused on future projects, rather than being project specific.

Customers are looking for a service which can add value to their operation. Construction organizations must provide a total package that offers the customer added value in a way the competition does not.

The customer survey

A questionnaire survey was conducted as part of the background research for this report to gauge the extent to which construction organizations are currently satisfying the needs of customers. The survey was sent to 250 customers, including central and local government, housing associations, education, property developers, and investors, together with owner occupiers, of which 91 responded.

The survey revealed a raft of issues which customers considered to be of particular importance on their projects, including advice on whole-life costs and economic life, the impact of technology on building service life, safety on site, the integration of information systems, and the early involvement of component manufacturers during the design phase of the project.

Selection of contractors

There was common agreement regarding the non-price factors that are critical in the selection of contractors. These include:

- past experience/reputation of the organization
- awareness of customers' needs and priorities
- trust
- organizational culture.

Lack of trust in the industry is a throwback to when customers felt they were likely to be 'stitched up' whenever they became involved in building by firms whose sole aim was to maximize profits. This had a major effect on how customers and outsiders perceive the construction industry.

Customers want

The demands of customers goes beyond the short-term requirements from a single project. Customers want:

- an industry that owns its problems and does not constantly keep hiding behind excuses

- an industry that understands and delivers what customers expect from their projects

- reasonable profits for construction organizations that reflect the risks that they are taking

- single-point responsibility

- projects that have sensible guarantees, where somebody clearly owns any problems which might arise after completion

- an end to the conflict mentality

- projects that use standard components which can be easily sourced and replaced at the end of their service life

- respect and trust for each others' work.

There has been little loyalty on any side in the past, as project after project is awarded to the lowest bidder.

Meeting customers' needs

A wide range of views concerning perceived weaknesses were expressed by customers, but there were also some good messages. The findings mirror closely those of other industry initiatives, including the Construction Clients' Forum . The following were considered to be particularly significant barriers to customer satisfaction.

- While consultants are satisfactory at understanding, communicating and presenting their clients' requirements effectively, almost two-thirds of the respondents believed the brief was often prepared too quickly and half of the respondents expressed concerns regarding errors and omissions.

- Construction firms frequently fail to understand the needs of their customers or to keep them fully informed as the project progresses. The majority of customers were indifferent when asked "how well do you consider that contractors understand your business needs?"

- The construction industry has failed to promote effective supply chain management by not tackling such problems as fragmentation, poor communication and coordination, and inefficient processes. Customers today expect the construction industry to adopt the modern commercial objectives of understanding its customers' needs and finding innovative solutions that yield savings and improved quality or value. They fear that supply chain management, in particular, is given insufficient emphasis and the results of worthwhile research are often poorly disseminated.

- Firms are slow to embrace innovative practices and fail to exploit the full potential of information technologies.

Despite the concerns, there was a positive note to the customer survey. Sixty percent of respondents expressed general satisfaction with the level of value-for-money provided by the construction industry, and it was frequently noted that the industry has made efforts to rectify shortcomings.

Innovation

Innovation takes many forms. The construction industry can work better for customers by:

- making the same product at a lower price
- making a better product at the same price
- making a new and better product, even at a higher price.

Against a backdrop of poor supply chain management, little standardization of design and high levels of defects, customers see innovation and research as vital to improving standards in UK construction. They are concerned that investment in research by the supply side of the industry has been dropping since 1990, while the research carried out focuses too much on product development and too little on their needs.

How can we do better?

Improving the industry through supply-side integration

One of the strengths of the UK system is flexibility, where designs can be developed during construction and changes can to be accommodated. Conversely, this strength is also one of the weaknesses of the UK system - it gives too much flexibility for change. Variations frequently occur well into the construction phase, introducing uncertainties into the project. For customers, certainty of cost and certainty of time are what matters.

If the industry is to improve performance and ensure certainty in the delivery of the final product it is essential that it:

- embraces all organizations within the procurement chain - each gains individual benefits through closer integration
- relies on the provision of timely and accurate data
- creates stable relationships, crucial for promoting trust and removing unnecessary transactions.
- integrates all players within the process to minimize the length and cost of the supply chain
- pays attention to scheduling, handling and storage of materials and components
- identifies where the problems are prior to work starting on site, and not after the work has started.

The supply chain is now much longer and more complex, with material manufacturers, component manufacturers, plant and equipment manufacturers, merchants, specialist contractors, trade contractors, and general contractors. A lot of knowledge resides with the various organizations about products and processes. How can information be captured and transferred throughout the chain effectively?

Answer: the promotion of trust, long-term commitment, and use of technology via common design and management systems.

Practical issues

When a small specialist contractor is asked to provide input to the design of a project, the practical issues are:

■ how can it be sure its ideas won't be used even if its bid is unsuccessful?

■ how can it be reimbursed for the time spent in giving the information?

Answer: trust and partnering with the organization, without trust and commitment, the industry will be stuck.

Competitive tendering will still be used but it will be based on a different set of criteria at the design stage.

Learning from other industries - Messages from Technology Foresight

Launched in 1994, Technology Foresight develops visions of the future to guide today's decision makers. It is about anticipating the future, identifying potential needs, threats and opportunities, and using the UK's strengths in science and technology. The reports produced by the programme covered 16 separate sectors:

- Agriculture, horticulture and forestry
- Chemicals
- Construction
- Defence and aerospace
- Energy
- Financial services
- Food and drink
- Health and life sciences

- IT, electronics and communications
- Leisure and learning
- Manufacturing, production and business services
- Marine
- Materials
- Natural resources and environment
- Retail and distribution
- Transport

From those reports it is possible to identify a number of key messages for the construction industry.

- Integration of design and production and integration across sectors is critical.
- Creation of a culture based on innovation is required - one that provides a constant flow of new and improved products, materials, processes and technologies to serve existing and future needs.
- Concurrent engineering, multi-disciplinary design and optimization tools will allow the early consideration of issues such as buildability, maintainability and whole-life costs with due regard for system performance.
- Total 'seamless' system solutions in response to customer demand will be the norm. A seamless system means a fully integrated system where the joins are not visible, i.e. the joins between design and construction, the joins between the contractor and the specialist contractor and the joins between dissimilar components.
- Materials suppliers and manufacturers will play an increasingly vital role in the supply chain and the performance of end products.
- Design should embrace customized solutions by using standard components which have the flexibility to accommodate a variety of uses and design solutions.
- Products with in-built 'intelligence' will be a key for the future of supply, fixing, repair and maintenance.

- The development of infrastructure that is intelligent and self-monitoring will mean more effective and economic repair and replacement programmes as well as improved energy efficiency.
- Crime is the biggest growth industry that designers must tackle.
- Telecommunications will be free to users.
- Environmental and regulatory standards will be increasingly stringent.
- It will be necessary to eliminate negative environmental impacts and to design for recyclability.
- Design must take into account whole-life costing and appraisal to ensure effective operation and maintenance throughout the design life of the facility and the subsequent reuse, recycling and disposal of goods.
- Disposal of construction waste will be a major issue, recycling of materials will be required.
- Energy efficiency is back on the agenda.
- Design must cater for an ageing population.
- There will be a new generation of new materials and biomaterials.
- There will be greater collaboration across supplier boundaries.

The construction industry must develop and implement new and updated methods of organization and working if is to achieve effective supply-side integration.

The most important is effective supply-chain management - management of the supply chain interfaces and information flows is essential for effective delivery of the product. As part of this process, the industry must focus on the principles of lean design and lean construction in the drive for design and construction integration and the elimination of waste from the process.

One inevitable question arising from this type of integration is who pays, and can there be a guarantee that organizations giving information to the design team will be successful in securing the work afterward?

Constructors can use rapid methods for prototyping and design completion to allow 90% design, cost and time certainty prior to any production commencing on site. This normally involves using electronic prototyping to 'build' the project in a computer prior to work starting on site. The involvement of suppliers and contractors is critical to this. Similarly, design coordination can be improved by placing heavier emphasis on early planning, eliminating unnecessary design iterations and reworking throughout the project.

Small construction firms and jobbing builders, with their strong network of local firms and local knowledge, will find this concept more difficult to accept or adopt. However, being a small organization does not prohibit innovation.

CRINE

CRINE (Cost Reduction Initiative for the New Era) is an industry-wide collaborative effort on the part of the oil and gas industry. It identifies three areas which contribute to North Sea oil development that cost in the region of four to six times more than counterparts in other oil and gas provinces.

- Design - it is important to ensure that front-end engineering takes place, that a project is defined fully and late design changes are eliminated.
- Materials and equipment.
- Methods, procedures and processes.

Comparisons show that costs for a particular rig installation in the North Sea were £103 million whereas in the Gulf of Mexico installation costs were £27 million. There is recognition of the fact that individual companies can reduce their costs.

There are many areas where joint action by the operators and supplies sector can lead to readily acceptable solutions.

Acheiving the vision

It is easy to offer the usual platitude, stating that the vision for the industry in the future is that "it will need to deliver projects on time, within budget and to a quality which leads to the customer's expectations being exceeded." The availability of many new techniques, however, does make it possible to advocate reengineering the business process to include concurrent engineering and continuous improvement, thereby moving towards achieving the vision. In particular, the industry can better serve the needs of customers by implementing the techniques of lean supply chain management.

This report recognizes the importance of:

- people

- process

- technology

- product

and their interrelationships.

Technology is a means to an end, it enables other processes to happen more effectively. Enabling technologies have a critical part to play in achieving the vision. These technologies will impact on designers, financiers, specialists, producers and contractors. All the enabling technologies which will impact on the construction industry in the future are currently available and have already been used. Importantly, people and cultural issues impact everything. Throughout this report, more general issues that include environmental and people issues are covered.

The remainder of this report is structured into three sections. First, mechanisms for improving product delivery through the adoption of lean design and lean supply are addressed. Second, the enabling technologies which will ensure the industry is able to meet future customer demands are considered. Third, issues of people and organizations are discussed.

The research team that produced this report have created in Chapter 6 a vision of construction in 2010.

Chapter 3
Improving product delivery

Improving product delivery means ensuring that the right goods get to the right place, at the right time, at the lowest appropriate cost and in the desired condition. Logistics was a concept first developed in the manufacturing industry as a tool to achieve control over deliveries. Although the nature of logistics varies considerably between organizations, the key elements are:

- transportation
- site planning - organization of goods/people
- customer service
- inventories
- protective packaging
- order processing and information flows
- warehousing
- facility location
- product scheduling
- materials handling
- disposal of packaging materials/waste.

An example of how logistics has been used to change the nature of manufacturing is the automotive industry's increased use throughout the 1990s of outsourcing for components and assemblies. Historically, the majority of fabrication was carried out in-house in an attempt to retain control of the process. Today, car manufacturers are nothing more than assemblers, accounting for only around 15% of the total manufacturing process (Figure 7 shows the changes in the automotive supply chain since the 1970s). Effective supply-chain management and logistics are now central to achieving integrated assembly.

With increasing product complexity, automotive components suppliers are now the main drivers of technological development within the supply chain. The need for joint planning, research and development has led to long-term ties between manufacturers and suppliers. These relationships have created greater certainty and predictability in the delivery of the final product.

The construction supply chain has many differences with the automotive supply chain, however we have much to learn.

Figure 7: Changes in the automotive supply chain

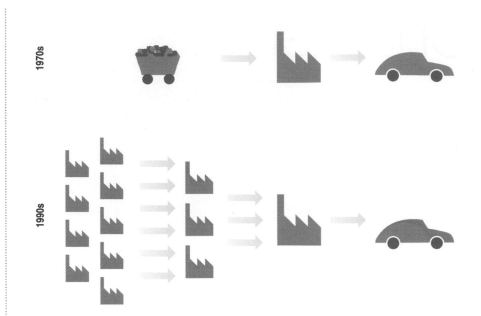

While the automotive industry has created certainty and stability in the supply chain, construction has not grasped the value of an effective supply chain and its role in the efficient delivery of the final product. The automotive sector has outsourced pre-assembled components and sub-assemblies, construction has been slow to follow suit. While some construction elements may now be prefabricated and assembled, a high proportion of the work is still fabricated on site, which creates uncertainty and a lack of predictability.

Supply chain management

Whereas logistics is a concept or theory, supply-chain management is the method through which the theory can be put into practice. The objective of supply-chain management is to improve efficiency of all processes involved in delivering a product or service. This is achieved by considering the roles of, and relationships between, all processes involved in delivering the final product; these range from design, through manufacturing and into production, installation and assembly. The supply chain embraces designers, material suppliers, production facilities, distributors and customers who are all linked by the flow of both materials and information. Value is added when materials are processed or passed on to subsequent stages within the supply chain, while costs are incurred directly by each process. The objective is to minimize cost and maximize added value. The construction industry must move towards a lean supply chain by eliminating unnecessary waste while improving the speed and certainty of delivery.

Achieving a lean process

Lean principles are associated with the drive towards the reduction of waste and have been successfully applied in the automotive industry in Japan, North America and Europe. Their purpose is to minimize use of everything - human effort, capital investment, facilities, inventories and time. There are five key principles which must be applied in order to develop a lean process:

- specify what does and does not create value for the customer
- identify all the steps necessary to design, order and produce the product across the whole value stream to highlight non value-adding activities
- streamline value creating activities to eliminate detours, backflows or waiting
- make only what is required by the customer and just-in-time
- strive for continuous improvement.

Design and construction organizations are project-based rather than product-based. Teams work together, then disband when a project is complete. There is little feedback or knowledge transfer into the next project.

Table 1: Comparing the changes in the automotive industry with construction

Automotive industry in the 1970s (Europe and USA)	Automotive industry in the 1990s (Europe and USA)	The construction industry in the 1990s (Europe and USA)
Highly vertically integrated, "make what you can in-house"	Major subsystems outsourced from major suppliers	Outsourcing is growing in every respect
Very wide, fragmented supplier base	Small number of preferred suppliers	Fragmented supply chain with a small number of preferred suppliers
Few partnerships	Trusted long-term relationships	Adversarial relationships
Some global products, mainly local	Global products / development	Some global products, mainly sourced locally
Little component re-use across models	Highly modularized across model range	Preference for bespoke solutions
Design undertaken by guru, often outside consultant	Design and production highly integrated using IT systems	Design and production normally divorced, especially legally
Communication paper-based	Electronic transactions	Communication paper-based
Whole-life cost and recycling not an issue	Whole life cost and performance and recycling very important	Whole-life costs not always considered fully during design
Servicing, maintenance and parts sales seen as an extra	Servicing, maintenance and after sales care seen as an integral part of the process	Maintenance seldom undertaken by contractor
Purchasing based on price	Purchasing based on service and reliability of performance	Tendering normally decided on price - not value
Purchase what technology is available to meet designated performance requirements	Integrating product technology from suppliers, work with the supplier to get continuous improvement	Suppliers tend to achieve continuous improvement despite fragmentation with their customers
Suppliers involved for the initial sale	Suppliers involved from concept to assembly	Suppliers rarely consulted early on in design
Standard product availability	Customization of the standard product	Highly customized product - often unnecessarily
Prototypes produced for testing	Prototypes tested in the computer prior to production of test model	Knowledge-based engineering and Intelligent CAD increasingly being used to 'test' an electronic prototype
Environmental issues not seen as important	Environment, safety, and security coming to the top of the agenda	Environmental and safety issues increasingly important drivers

Supply chain management main barriers and obstacles (Source: Financial Times)

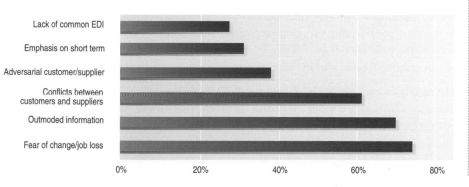

The experience gained by the completion of projects must be fed into future projects.

Wastage of materials on site, for whatever reason, is still too high.

Lean principles in construction

Relationships between contractors, customers and suppliers can currently be described as ad hoc collaborations, which is clearly not conducive to establishing effective teams or to the application of the principles of a lean process.

The construction industry continues to overlook the roles of design and design coordination within the overall logistical process. The design process is seldom undertaken with the production process in mind. For example, the early and accurate scheduling of materials is frequently impossible because the original details have a limited value, either because they are not complete at the commencement of a contract, or there are considerable variations before the contract has started. This is not only because the principles of lean design have not been embraced, but also due to the lack of constructive feedback from other projects.

The supply of building materials and components to site continues to be fraught with obstacles which have a significant effect on productivity levels. Building materials often require large storage capacity, that is rarely available on most sites. Where storage facilities are provided, the conditions in which the materials are kept can lead to damage, such as from the ingress of weather or from the movement of people, plant and equipment. The resultant loss and wastage of construction materials indicate that lean concepts are rarely applied.

The construction industry must embrace the principles of lean design and lean supply.

Lean design

Ease of construction will not come about by accident, instead it will be the result of implementing a lean design process. There are four basic techniques to lean design.

- Leadership - someone with the power to champion a project whose job it is to design and engineer a project.

- Teamwork - a tightly knit team containing members from the core professions who are responsible throughout the development and construction process is essential.

- Communication - critical design trade-offs often fail to be resolved until very late in the project. Being able to confront conflicts at an early stage is therefore essential.

- Simultaneous development - ensuring that the various professions are in direct contact with each other from the early stages of design, accompanied by the development of long-term relationships, makes it possible to anticipate the actions of others and act accordingly.

The construction industry can begin to address the principles of lean design by considering two fundamental issues.

The first is the time taken to prototype and complete new designs. Improved methods of rapid prototyping and design completion are required, which could allow 90% design, cost and time certainty prior to any production commencing on site. The 90% complete does not necessarily imply a design–bid–build project, it is equally achievable through overlapping design and production using fee-based procurement. Rapid completion of design is currently hampered in the UK by the tendency to approach every design solution with a blank sheet of paper, resulting in the use of non-standard equipment, materials and procedures, which add cost as well as time.

UK customers and planning authorities like individualistic design, that is what they are used to. System building in the 1970s failed because people did not want their projects to look the same. What has changed is the ability to customize standard components, thus giving the freedom for individualistic design.

The nature of design

There has always been some confusion about the boundaries between the three elements that together constitute the act of designing a building, which has often led many people to claim to be a building's designer:

- to conceive the spatial arrangements within a building so that its functions and external appearance that are as customer desires

- to conceive the means by which these plans may be built

- to be able to justify before construction commences that the previous two goals can be achieved, given the constraints of, for example, technical feasibility, life expectancy, cost and completion date.

Fundamental to these three elements is the act of people or organizations communicating ideas to one another. If the whole process goes on in one mind, it is the work of the craftsman, not of designing in the sense used in the building industry today. This process of communication inevitably means that there is an observable division of labour - one person conceives a scheme, another carries out what has been conceived. Apart from contractual differences, it matters not if the communication is between individuals, separate firms or departments within one firm.

Case for change - Rolls-Royce

It seems that 50 years ago products were developed more quickly than they are today. This is because:

- products have grown in complexity
- organizational structures have grown in complexity
- the application of technology to the product has grown in complexity.

These factors have led to complex procedures and processes which result in non value-added activities. Rolls-Royce has simplified systems by changing data into knowledge through electronic technology and by implementing teaming arrangements to remove organizational barriers. Electronic mock-ups have replaced physical prototypes, resulting in improved 'right first time' quality.

The second issue is the coordination of design. Heavier emphasis on early planning is required to eliminate unnecessary design iterations and reworking. As the choice of components and materials continues to increase and construction becomes ever more complex, specialist input from manufacturers and suppliers at the early stages of design will become essential if construction is to move towards the principles of lean design.

Delivering lean design

Delivering lean design requires the implementation of two principles of lean processes:

- eliminating non value-adding activities
- making the remaining value-creating steps more efficient.

As it is becoming clear that tasks are accomplished more effectively when the product is worked on continuously from initiation to completion, the result is the fight against departmentalized thinking and so elimination of functions and departments. The application of information technology in design will be essential if the industry is to achieve 90% design completion before work starts on site. Better design solutions will come about as designers, contractors, specialists and suppliers work together with common IT infrastructures. These enable joint investigation of the effects of conceptual decisions on fabrication, transportation, buildability, erection costs and project feasibility.

Lean supply

The following observations were extracted from a questionnaire survey of 250 (thirty percent response) suppliers, builders' merchants, component manufacturers and contractors, conducted to ascertain supply chain practice.

- None of the suppliers or merchants surveyed reported involvement in projects before the commencement of tendering. However, the majority considered that early involvement would be beneficial to avoid problems which might arise from the placement of incorrect or incomplete specifications.

- Most of the merchants and specialist suppliers felt that designers did not want them involved in the design process.

- There was a lack of trust between suppliers and contractors, fueled by the unwillingness of contractors or subcontractors to pay for quotes or worked drawings and the late payment of bills. (Lean supply only works if suppliers get paid properly.)

The disruptive effect of fluctuating workloads in the construction industry, caused by the boom–bust cycle, has exacerbated the reliance on ad hoc planning for the supply of materials, leading to several problems:

- Materials may be purchased only immediately before they are required, resulting in delays and interruptions to the work schedule.

- Materials may be procured in larger quantities than actually needed on site, resulting in wastage during stocking, handling and transporting.

- Disruption of supplies often creates supply bottlenecks, making the planned flow of materials even more difficult if not impossible to manage effectively and efficiently.

Technology clusters: integrating suppliers within the process

The idea of using technology clusters to integrate the supply chain offers a way of introducing lean thinking to the design process. Suppliers and specialists working to a detailed design have little opportunity or incentive to suggest improvements based on their own experiences. Organizing suppliers into vertical chains and playing them off against each other in search of the lowest cost will block the flow of information horizontally between suppliers. Suppliers must be given the opportunity to decrease their costs through improved organization and process innovation.

A three-step approach for developing technology clusters was described in the Reading Construction Forum's report *Value for Money*.

Step 1- The project is broken into manageable pieces. The production process is defined in terms of a highly focused set of 'technology clusters.' Each technology cluster addresses a complete set of functional systems within the building, e.g. structure, envelope or primary service systems. Within each technology cluster, the client, designers, production managers and specialist trade contractors are involved from the stage of project conception, and collaborate to provide the best solution - a response to the client's requirement based on fully integrated design and production. A paramount requirement is to bring those with production responsibility into active collaboration with designers at the front-end of projects.

Step 2 - A building typically has five or six technology clusters which must be coordinated as a whole to ensure the overall value of the design and production process is conserved. A group comprising the client, lead designer and production manager provides this coordination throughout the project, and ensures the overall value chain which links the constituent technology clusters is maintained.

Step 3 - The transfer of knowledge by participating organizations is the third step to success. Although each specific project must achieve high value targets, there is usually little time for long-term learning. Organizations must take an active responsibility to educate their staff and train them to contribute their specialist knowledge and interface intelligently and effectively with their counterparts. Production success depends creative collaboration.

Through technology clusters, the relevant skills can be accessed in a focused way and brought together at a project location for short periods of time. By focusing on the technology cluster, the value in the chain of progressive effort to produce each building system is maintained.

Implementing lean supply

Successful implementation of lean supply is often hampered by:

- failure to obtain commitment from top management

- inadequate education programmes

Technology clusters in the automotive industry

In lean projects, bottlenecks are overcome and waste is eliminated by all the necessary suppliers being selected at the very outset. In the automotive industry this is done by developing a clustered structure (Womack, Jones & Roos, 1990). First-tier suppliers are responsible for working as an integral part of the product development team. They are given a performance specification, and then left to decide for themselves as to the best engineering solution. They are encouraged to share information among themselves about ways to improve the design process, and because each supplier specializes in one type of component, the sharing of information is mutually beneficial. Each first-tier supplier then forms a second tier of suppliers under itself. Companies in the second tier are assigned the task of fabricating individual parts. These suppliers are usually manufacturing specialists with little expertise in product engineering, but with strong backgrounds in process engineering and plant operations.

This clustered structure has been successfully applied to the construction industry by Rover Group in the construction of their design facilities.

- inadequate external assistance

- underestimating the task of implementation

- inappropriate time scale for implementation

- failure to integrate the process and control operations

- lack of software and appropriate integration with the financial system

- failure to appreciate lean supply as a long-term on-going process.

Figure 8 shows a comparison of past and present in the automotive industry, an industry that demonstrates that lean supply principles can be put into practice. Suppliers to the automotive industry are now involved at the outset of projects and through to manufacture and, ultimately, maintenance. An enabler in this process is IT.

Delivery and lean supply

The quality and accuracy of information have a critical role to play in the lean supply chain. Inaccurate or untimely data concerning stock and deliveries and a poor flow of financial information can have adverse effects on the efficient planning of the supply chain.

Effective management of information within the construction industry is hampered by reliance on primitive paper-based systems. Communications and data capture technologies have a key role to play in the integration and free flow of information between departments and organizations. However, they should not be implemented in isolation, but rather as part of a common infrastructure. Processes which do not add value must be eliminated. The remaining processes and activities can then be transformed by the implementation of new technologies.

Lean organization must come before high-tech process automation. High-tech solutions that are improperly organized cause more problems than they remove. For most production operations only 5% of activities add value, 35% are necessary non value-adding activities given the existing technology, and 60% add no value at all. Eliminating all non value-adding activities is the greatest potential.

Figure 8: The past and the present - integrating the supplier into the process

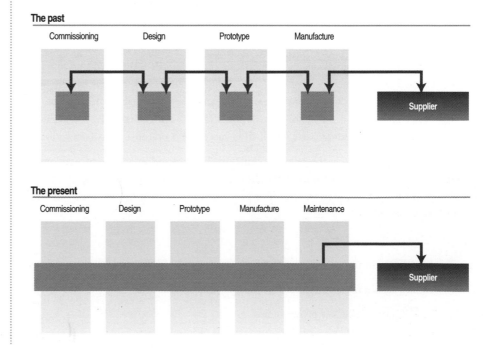

Minimizing waste and the environmental effects of construction

Skanska, one of the leading construction companies in Europe and North America, focused on the problem of wastage of materials. During 1996 its waste management costs totalled £10 million. Cost reductions made by using made-to-measure materials, carrying out at-source waste separation and selective demolition has reduced waste-related costs by an average of 30%. The previous use of non made-to-measure materials had meant that about 20% more materials had to be transported, handled, recycled or discarded.

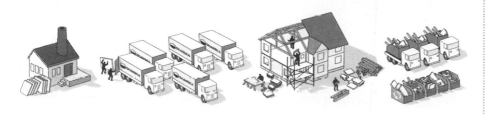

Traditional materials management

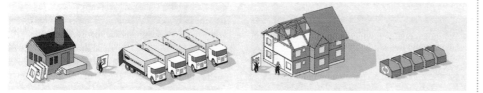

Skanska improved materials management

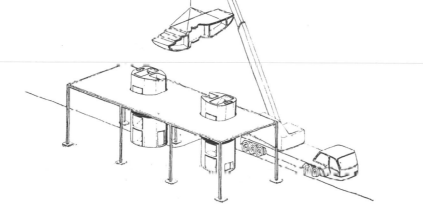

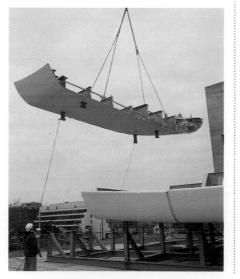

Analysis of waste from construction sites

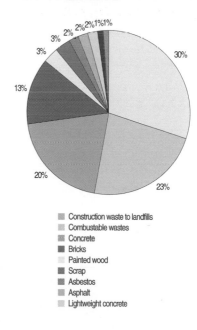

- Construction waste to landfills
- Combustable wastes
- Concrete
- Bricks
- Painted wood
- Scrap
- Asbestos
- Asphalt
- Lightweight concrete

Chapter 4
Using technology for process improvement

The word 'technology' comes from the Greek 'tekhnologia' which means systematic treatment and describes the use of scientific knowledge for practical purpose.

Technology: 1 the application of practical sciences to industry or commerce; 2 the methods, theory and practices governing such application; 3 the total knowledge and skills available to any human society for industry, art, science, etc.

Technology impacts upon all people, products and processes in an economy; its application is one of the drivers of change for the next wave of economic growth. However, as the Construction Task Force's report (1998) stated:

"Technology on its own cannot provide the answer to the need for greater efficiency and quality in construction ... first sort out the culture, then define and improve the processes and finally apply technology as a tool."

An awareness of available technology and an ability to apply it is often more important than being the pioneer of a new product or a process. It is very difficult in construction to patent new processes, so competitive advantages must be sought through more successful application of available technology. For example, trenchless technology has benefits for installation of utilities - it is no longer necessary to dig up streets to install services. Trenchless technology was pioneered by the plant and equipment manufacturers, but the benefits accrue to the customers and contractors.

The focus of this chapter is on the use of technology as a tool to enable improvement. Technology is vitally important for the future, but people will not use it simply because it is there. Technology has to be shown to have benefits. The key areas of technological innovation and their potentials for application in construction are outlined to highlight which areas of innovation organizations should be looking to develop in their quest to remain competitive in the future.

There are four important messages for construction organizations to bear in mind when developing strategies for dealing with innovation:

1. **Tried and tested technology** - be aware of technology and know how it is developing, not just in construction but also in other industries. A lot of technology that could be useful to construction can be found in the aerospace, automotive and shipbuilding industries - organizations have to engage in the creative swiping of good ideas.

'Technology is an enabler which helps to change the culture and improve the process."

'Technology is a slave not a master.'

'Technology does not create fear for young people.'

2. **Enabling technology** - embrace new technologies that allow an existing process or activity to be carried out more effectively or efficiently, or may allow a new product or service to be developed. For example, new technology makes the decontamination of contaminated land feasible, releasing land which would not previously have been usable for construction. Similarly, the use of satellites for telecommunications increasingly makes cabling unnecessary.

3. **Appropriateness** - focus on appropriate technology (fitness for purpose). It is important to ensure that the ability to maintain and operate the technology is available, which comes about by providing technology that is functional, operable and maintainable.

4. **The shift from data to information to knowledge** - consider how information technology has evolved in stages, from providing data, then information and now knowledge. Data are the building blocks of the information economy (or as Robert Lucky of AT & T Bell Laboratories says: "they are the unorganized sludge" of the information age). Information is data that have been organized into meaningful patterns - vast amounts of data are processed into information. Business becomes knowledge-based by putting information to productive use. Just as information has superseded data, so knowledge will supersede information. Knowledge, and intelligence, must be introduced into products used in construction. For example, Goodyear has developed a smart tyre which contains a microchip that collects and analyses data about air pressure; the aim is to send a message to the dashboard giving the driver information about tyre pressures.

Enabling technologies
Incorporating knowledge into construction

Knowledge is information put to productive use. Davis and Botkin (1994) illustrate the concept by the example of a tennis racket that glows where the ball strikes it, to help the player correct their stroke. Likewise, knowledge is in a nappy that changes colour when it is wet. Both examples are of products that take information about what is happening to them and communicate it to the consumer in a practical way. In themselves they are not earth-shattering products, but consider if the principle were applied to building components and products. For example, flat roofs that change colour where they are leaking; concrete and blocks which have radio frequency tags embedded in them to give their specifications, so aiding refurbishment or disposal; paint which changes colour where it cracks, showing stress points in a structure. Some companies, such as manufacturers of lifts, are already incorporating knowledge into products.

Materials technologies

Future developments in materials technologies will impact on construction in a number of areas. One in particular is the use of 'smart' materials to enable users to filter and interpret information more effectively. Such technologies are likely to draw on materials science, biotechnology, biomimetics, nanotechnology and artificial intelligence. Advances are also expected in the development of structural materials, jointing methods, advanced composites, lightweight materials, advanced coatings, knowledge-based materials, energy-efficient materials and recyclable and reusable materials.

A good example is the development of advanced composite materials, high-strength fibre-reinforced polymer materials which are now established as important materials for use alongside steel, concrete, aluminium and timber. Lightweight advanced composite materials, used on their own or with other materials, can be shaped into high-quality modular systems in the factory. This provides a new opportunity for

IT in UK construction

Of UK construction professionals:

■ 83% have access to a PC

■ 50% have a CD-rom on their machine

■ 25% have access to the Internet

■ more than 50% expect their expenditure on IT to increase

■ all professions use CAD.

Source: Construct IT - Centre of Excellence

construction to move towards lean manufacturing off site and helps the industry in its move to convert raw materials into high-quality finished products at the lowest possible on-cost. The lightweight nature of an advanced composite structure, coupled with its improved resistance to corrosion, has benefits in whole-life cost.

As part of the move towards lean design and manufacturing, a new way of thinking about dealing with new materials is needed - but how? Direct material replacement for steel or concrete may not be the best approach.

Information technology

Technologies designed for data transfer, data capture and data manipulation will be among the most significant enabling technologies to the construction industry. They could have profound impacts on both design and construction.

Data transfer

Developments in electronic commerce have radically altered the way information can be passed between organizations. A raft of technologies, including electronic data interchange (EDI), the Internet, intranet and e-mail, are revolutionizing the trading process between construction firms, impacting on the way designers, suppliers and contractors do business, and are allowing greater integration between the customer, designer and contractor in the on-going decision making process.

Data capture

The construction process demands that information on physical components is gathered during each stage of the supply chain, including delivery information, installation instructions, commissioning data and maintenance instructions. Developments in data capture technologies allow such data to be stored within a barcode or radio frequency electronic tag, supporting decision making procedures by passing the information through the supply chain.

Data manipulation

Developments in intelligent computer aided design (ICAD), knowledge-based engineering (KBE) and object modelling (OM) offer the ability to integrate design, manufacture and installation more closely than ever before. Building a project in a computer prior to construction work starting on site has long been a dream, but electronic prototyping is fast becoming a reality. Drawings can be displayed in 3D with full dimensions and the ability to rotate the object and view it from all directions. Specialist firms, such as structural steelwork constructors, simulate their construction sequences to look for clashes with other activities or other parts of designs. However, the process can be scaled up to encompass a complete project.

Such systems offer the advantages of early visualization of completed projects to customers, rapid prototyping of designs and more effective information exchange between project participants, in particular the opportunity to team manufacturers with designers during the early prototype stages.

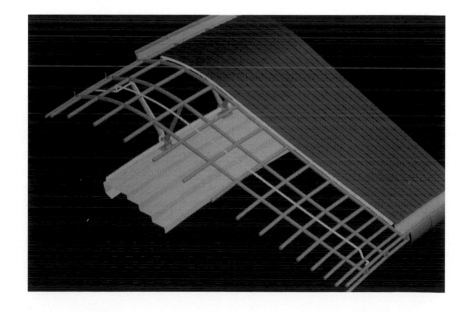

Making a start: CORENET

CORENET is an automatic plan checking system used in Singapore. The system is part of IT2000, Singapore's IT Master Plan aimed at reengineering the business processes in the construction industry by using enabling technology to achieve a quantum leap in turnaround time, productivity and quality.

The systems involved aim to automate the checking process for the various plan types. They are leading edge systems that need the integration of expert knowledge, artificial intelligence and computer-aided design.

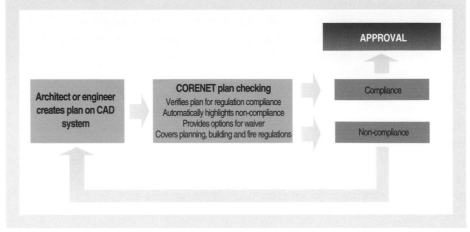

Information technologies in the lean design process

Improving customer briefing is the first step towards lean design. The way in which customer briefing (whereby the specific demands that the construction industry must meet are defined) is conducted inevitably has a direct influence on the industry's performance. A survey of customers showed that briefs are frequently prepared too quickly and contain too many errors and omissions.

It is envisaged that by 2010 a range of software packages focusing on the initial briefing stages will be available. These packages would help in identifying customer needs and could be linked to design visualization systems. IT can help support the capture of customer requirements and lead to the automated generation of alternative specifications.

Based on research and detailed case studies, a flowchart of the early stages of the briefing process has been developed (Figure 9) incorporating these software developments. Its focus is on the customer's needs and not on construction or the needs of the construction industry.

Visualization

Where a CAD model is combined with a visualization package, high-quality representations can be quickly produced within a virtual environment. However, computer-aided visualization does not only provide customers and designers with a powerful tool for exploring the aesthetic aspects of building design. Changes to designs can be made and viewed almost instantaneously, allowing the customer to explore a myriad of possible design trade-offs relating to quality, cost and time. This could have a profound impact on all phases within the design process by increasing the possibility of optimum design and reducing the time necessary for processing design iterations. A greater interaction between designer and customer is possible with the use of visualization packages, especially for final details when materials and finishes can be modelled to determine colour schemes and atmosphere.

The use of a visualization package can help first-time customers gain confidence in their design teams quickly by allowing them to visualize at an early stage the buildings they are proposing to buy.

Figure 9: Effective briefing process

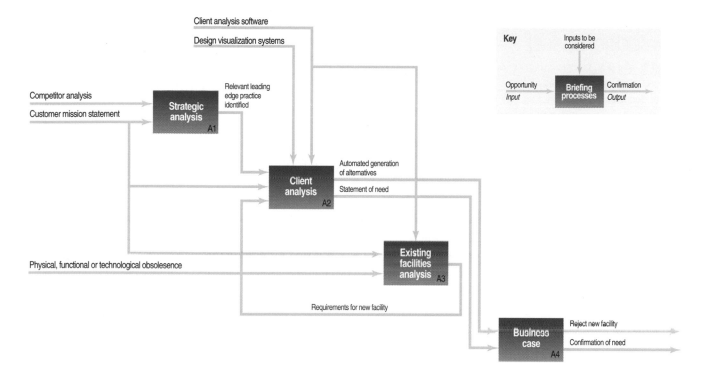

Computer aided, three dimensional interactive application (CATIA) was used in the development of Boeing's 777 passenger aircraft

This enabled:

- the assembly of parts to be simulated

- visualization of the product before it was made

- 100% pre-assembly on computer

- 50-80% reduction in non-conformance and the elimination of:

    misalignments

    interface difficulties

    costly mock-ups

- design to be carried out concurrently rather than sequentially

- specialists to be involved in the early design stage

- unnecessary complexity of parts to be eliminated.

Research has shown that the customers believe that project briefs are often prepared too quickly and frequently contain errors. Effective strategic, client and existing-facilities analysis are all crucial to preparing a good business case. By the year 2010, it is envisaged that a range of tailored software packages will allow the professional team to identify customer needs. Design visualization systems will play a crucial role in the briefing process.

Object modelling and knowledge-based engineering

An object model is an electronic representation of an individual building element, such as a door, wall or window. Attached to each object is a series of attributes which describe its particular physical characteristics or behaviour, including geometry, position, orientation, material, specification, cost and relationship with other objects. The model contains all information that may be required by the architect, structural engineer, quantity surveyor or contractor.

Schindler - developments in knowledge-based engineering

Due to frequent late changes in specification, Swiss lifts manufacturer Schindler has developed a visualization tool which produces fully rendered views of its catalogue products to allow customers to see what their chosen items will look like when finished. The system generates the complete specification for the lift, allowing the customer to sign off the order or take away a hard copy for final approval. The lift car is modelled in an intelligent computer aided design package using knowledge-based engineering. Output from the prototype can be in two forms:

- a 3D block diagram giving the functional relationship of components, to assist in communicating the engineering details

- a 3D rendered image for visualization purposes.

An advantage of this system is that any configuration options are automatically constrained by the engineering rules upon which the lift design is based. Also, there is limitless potential for expanding the system and integrating it with drawing production and generating a bill of quantities. It is envisaged that future developments will see the system encompass the automated production of costs, builders' work details and extension to other lift ranges.

Video conferencing

On the Bovis Bluewater shopping centre, project video conferencing has been used to hold meetings between the UK and Australia. There is also a video camera installed at the site offices. This transmits real-time images of project progress to the client's offices in Australia.

During object-oriented design (OOD) individual object models can be linked together to form sub-assemblies or larger building elements. For instance, door, wall, window, roof and floor objects could be linked to form a 'room object.' A key feature of this process is that the characteristics of the parent object are determined solely by the individual characteristics of its constituent elements. Thus, having defined the room object, the designer will have automatic access to compound cost data derived from the individual performance characteristics. KBE systems further extend the versatility of OM. KBE systems store not only objects but also rules that govern their assembly. For example, the structural engineer will be immediately alerted if the load attributes of a wall object exceed the load-bearing characteristics of a lintel object.

One of the major advantages of this approach is that once defined, component objects can be used in a variety of different design scenarios. This means that the inception of a new design does not necessarily mean starting from scratch; instead an overall solution can rapidly be assembled from an existing library. The ability to control the way in which objects are assembled offers the possibility of further dramatic reductions in design times. Both OOD and KBE offer real opportunities for the design team to achieve 90% design completion before work commences on site.

With 3D designs and object-oriented models being freely available and transferred over the Internet, multinational design teams acting as a single virtual unit can develop. These will further break down international barriers as local projects are increasingly sourced globally.

Using IT in the design process

The use of IT in the design process will bring about substantial savings in product definition and design by the use of knowledge based engineering. The result will be reduced lead times, enabling the constructed facility to be brought to the market that much quicker. Improvements will be made in:

- Working up of the design from concept through to detail will be much shorter

- Rapid prototyping - designers will be able to explore further options which reflect better trade-offs. This facility will also allow rapid re-design of components by integrating design and construction knowledge into a single product model, thereby allowing issues to be resolved concurrently and waste associated with rework to be reduced.

Multimedia communications

The improved speed and quality of information communication should pay dividends for an industry which is geographically dispersed and engages a multitude of organizations in the delivery of its products. Developments in high-speed data communications, such as ISDN (integrated services digital network), are set to radically alter communications between professionals and data exchange within design and construction. Benefits include:

- common CAD systems, which allow project partners to view and update building models simultaneously from geographically remote locations

- desk top video conferencing, which allows remote experts and project partners to conduct impromptu meetings.

Multimedia communications in particular offer a vehicle for rapid problem resolution as activities on-site progress. Problems or queries raised by site staff can be relayed direct to all relevant project professions to effect a rapid response. Video conferencing

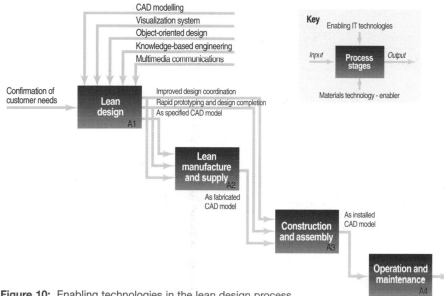

Figure 10: Enabling technologies in the lean design process

allows a variety of information to be exchanged simultaneously, including voice, video, CAD drawings and other images pertinent to the project. For example, video footage or still images illustrating specific problems which have arisen on-site can be viewed by any member of the project team from any location.

A number of developments are envisaged within this area, including mobile video transmission of live images from the site to the remote offices of designers or other experts. A prototype video transmission system has been developed by British Telecom which allows a roaming site cameraman to relay both voice and video in real-time. Further developments may culminate in the availability of a 'multimedia hard hat' which would allow hands-free filming.

Multimedia communications offer increased productivity for designers and engineers as they can spend less time travelling to and from sites and, because project participants need only attend meetings which relate specifically to their input, can reduce the time spent attending meetings.

Enabling technologies in the lean supply chain

The need to track construction materials reliably has stimulated a growing interest in automated materials management and inventory control systems. While most manufacturers and large builders' merchants now maintain computerized records for ordering products and stock control, these advances have not been matched by the technologies required to feed their information requirements. Computers rely on data, and the successful implementation of any system depends on the speed and accuracy of data collection and exchange.

Primitive paper-based forms remain the most common method for recording and transmitting information in construction. There are a variety of stages within the trading cycle when it is necessary to transmit or record information relating to physical products or components, including off-site manufacture, dispatch, delivery and site installation. Paper-based trading severely limits the timelines of information within the supply chain. In addition, information contained within orders, invoices and delivery notes must also be re-entered into the recipient's computer system. Even when keyboard entry is practical, the rate of data entry is low and errors are frequent. The bottleneck of information inevitably affects the cost and timelines, forcing operatives to spend unnecessary periods of time recording information which is secondary to their main task. Current reliance on paper-based trading is likely to hamper any notions of just-in-time and lean production / construction.

Developments in CAD modelling, visualization, knowledge-based engineering and multimedia communications techniques will all impact upon the lean design process. These technologies will enable rapid prototyping and design completion and facilitate improved coordination with manufacturers, suppliers and installers. The electronic CAD model generated during lean design will be used and modified during each subsequent supply chain phase to ensure continuity of information.

Enabling technologies in the lean supply chain can deliver reduced waste, lower costs and more accurate information provision. Internet applications, EDI, global positioning systems and barcoding or electronic tagging can be employed during manufacture, construction, operation and maintenance to manage construction products and components more effectively than ever before.

Electronic commerce can be used to improve materials handling and ensure that a quality product is delivered on time at the right price. This is achieved by using a range of technologies that permit more rapid and accurate data capture, storage and communication between supply chain partners (EDI, database systems and barcoded packaging). Figure 11 shows how information can flow electronically between manufacturers, suppliers and contractors.

The realities of life

How can information technology help a builder undertaking a small project in an urban area who does not want to spend large sums of money on equipment?

Answer: Most organizations will have access to a PC, use of an Internet connection means that they will be able to browse merchants' electronic catalogues, check prices and availability, and other materials. The whole transaction is electronic.

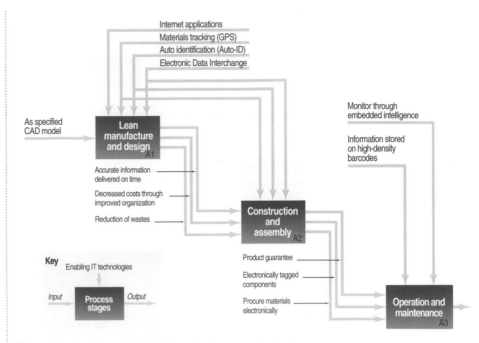

Figure 11: Enabling technologies in the lean supply chain

There is a solution to the data processing problems facing the construction industry. Recent advances in electronic commerce have radically altered the way in which trading information can be passed between organizations. The combination of a range of processes, such as EDI, e-mail and Internet applications, can yield dramatic improvements in the timeliness, accuracy and cost of conducting business. For example, a supplier who sends an invoice direct to the purchaser by EDI eliminates the delay of the postal system and the need for retyping and filing.

Even in a completely electronic trading environment, the problem of gathering information relating to physical product and components remains. Automated identification (Auto-ID) could yield radical improvements in managing and providing such information. These technologies use labels or tags to provide electronically readable information about a physical product during any stage within the supply chain. They are designed to provide significant efficiency gains over manual data capture and entry. A number of well established technologies can be considered for use within the construction industry, including barcoding and electronic tagging.

Electronic trading has been implemented extensively within retailing, automotive manufacture and aerospace. Although other sectors have achieved significant cost savings by using EDI and Auto-ID, the current level of use within the construction industry is low. These technologies have been used in a limited number of construction applications, including materials control, inventory and scheduling, but have been restricted to individual organizations and specific stages within the construction process.

Electronic commerce in construction

Builders' merchants and manufacturers are increasingly combining electronic trading with allied technologies to replace traditional methods of conducting business. EDI is used to transmit trading messages between partners (either traditional EDI or Internet-based solutions). Barcoding is used in any instance where it is necessary to confirm orders, delivery notes or invoices against physical products. Barcoding also allows merchants to automate sales with electronic point of sales (EPOS) systems. Scanning barcode labels attached to products allows price information to be automatically retrieved from the stores' database - triggering the transmittal of an electronic order to the manufacturer when stocks become low. Users frequently report significant savings, including:

- reduced cost of capturing data

- reduced paperwork

- manpower savings for processing invoices and other information

- improved accessibility to data

- avoidance of re-keying information into computer systems

- fewer errors in information recording and handling.

A key factor in encouraging greater uptake of electronic commerce in the UK construction supply chain is the development and implementation of industry-wide standards. A number of organizations are currently developing electronic commerce standard message formats within a variety of interest areas. The Builders' Merchants Federation (BMF) has launched an initiative called MERNET to promote the use of EDI within the construction materials supply chain which links manufacturers, distributors and suppliers. A software package links all standard message formats developed for electronic trading within construction. Increasing numbers of builders' merchants and manufacturers are choosing to trade using electronic commerce.

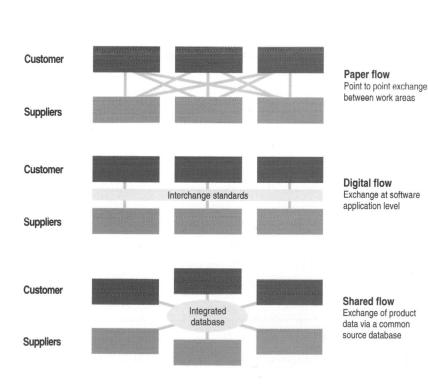

Paper flow
Point to point exchange between work areas

Digital flow
Exchange at software application level

Shared flow
Exchange of product data via a common source database

Using barcoding for materials management

Richard Lees, a manufacturer of precast/prestressed concrete floor beams, uses barcoding to identify and track individual products in an on-site yard. The company had previously relied on a manual system for recording the location of each beam. The high throughput of stock and slow speed of processing meant that records were frequently out of date.

Each beam and storage location now has a unique barcode. Portable scanners link directly with a central database, ensuring that records are constantly up-to-date. Within one year of the system becoming fully operational the company was able to recoup its initial capital outlay. The key benefits gained included:

- reduced cost of data entry at various stages of the delivery process, including 70% time saving in checking beams prior to delivery and an 85% saving in clerical data entry times

- improved records of beam locations resulting in a 30% time saving in locating beams within the storage yard.

Figure 12: The development from paper-based systems to an integrated database. The integrated database is at the heart of both lean design and lean supply. Organizations need to be able to access information and use knowledge to add value to the process.

Intelligent packaging and smart tagging

Tracking goods from the point of manufacture via warehouses to the point of sale and the generation of orders from purchases require technological support. Intelligent packaging and smart tagging have been developed with this specific purpose in mind. They can be used to benefit both the customer and the supply chain and can easily be applied to the construction industry.

Source: Technology Foresight - Retail Industry

Using enabling technologies in operation and maintenance

A recurring problem for maintenance engineers is the inability to access reliable and in-depth information about products or assemblies when on location. Information about plant, distribution and cabling systems can be complex and involve sizeable amounts of data provided by the manufacturer. Added to this is the maintenance history which accrues to each and every item within a facility.

Taylor Woodrow has developed a low-cost method for making both product information and maintenance history accessible on the job. Portable computing and high-capacity barcoding have been combined to provide practical benefits for a maintenance management programme by automating existing procedures and improving the availability of maintenance data in the field. Under the maintenance contract evaluated, a total capital outlay was recouped by direct-cost savings within a period of two and a half years.

Armitage Shanks reported that every item which leaves its factory is barcoded with a standard barcode label. This system was introduced to allow the organization to link electronic trading information with physical deliveries of prepackaged products. Pilkington Glass uses both EDI and barcoding during post-production management. Barcodes are attached to glass packs at the end of the production line - providing a unique identifier which allows access to EDI information and instructions during handling, stock control, dispatch and distribution. In both cases, the adoption of electronic trading technologies has partly been a reaction to changing requirements of the builders' merchants sector.

The process flowchart in figure 13 shows how electronic commerce can be used to improve handling of materials and ensure that a quality product is delivered on time at the right price. The flowchart incorporates the principles of logistics and electronic trading.

Trends in the UK construction supply chain - results of a survey

A telephone survey of 100 major UK construction supply chain organizations was undertaken to gauge the level of use of some of the key technologies that underpin electronic commerce. The results revealed interesting variations between contractors, suppliers and manufacturers.

- Over the past five years there has been a significant increase in overall levels of application of electronic communication technologies (local area networks, wide area networks and e-mail) across the industry (a trend reflected in all sectors of the supply chain).

- Over half of the organizations reported they were using EDI for electronic commerce, however most of these were the larger manufacturers and suppliers - contractors have been slow to embrace electronic commerce, a poor level of computer literacy was often blamed for this.

- The majority of small builders' merchants used computer-based programs to hold their stock records, though these were rarely sophisticated enough to place orders directly with the manufacturers - the majority of orders were placed direct by phone, fax or letter.

- Only one-third of organizations reported using any form of auto-ID technology - all used barcoding to label materials and components. The majority of these organizations were either manufacturers or suppliers. Significantly, only 5% of contractors that responded to the survey reported any use of Auto-ID techniques.

- The major driving force that attracts construction supply-chain organizations to use electronic commerce is the ability to reduce levels of paperwork

Figure 13: Using electronic commerce to reengineer materials handling

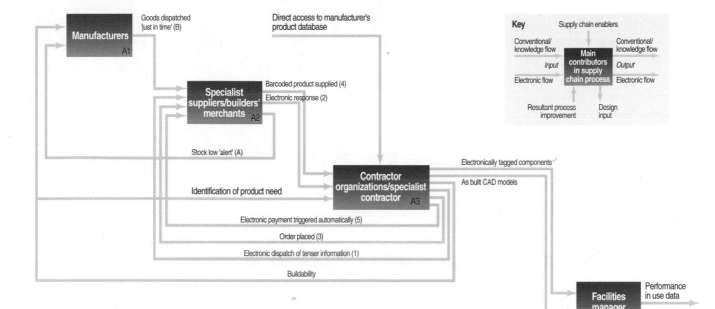

(invoices, orders, delivery notes, etc.), together with reducing the costs of capturing, processing and transferring trading information.

In conclusion, the main issue raised by the survey was the lack of awareness of the costs and benefits of electronic commerce. The size of firms appears to have an influence on the take-up of electronic commerce. There may be a strong argument for electronic commerce service providers to enter the construction market to help small and medium enterprises cope with the technology.

Some of the real life barriers to innovation

- Construction is a project based industry, therefore innovations are frequently evaluated on an individual project basis. However, because technology adds value to activities rather than delivering direct benefits, it is often difficult to establish the bottom line. It is normally difficult for construction organizations to justify investments that do not provide a short-term return.

- Application of an innovative technology by one firm may have far-reaching consequences for other organizations in the supply chain. Fragmentation within the industry means that these benefits are not always embraced in the evaluation process.

- Customers, contractors and consultants frequently pay lip service to innovation and the application of new technologies. "I'm all in favour of innovation - but not on my job!"

Strategies for promoting improved supply chain management

One of the two key strategies for encouraging wider uptake of electronic commerce technologies is to increase awareness within the industry. An industry-wide education initiative that combines a number of demonstration projects could achieve this goal. Particular efforts should be made to increase awareness among contracting organizations, which appear to be lagging behind manufacturers and suppliers.

The second strategy is for influential organizations who have the power to enforce the use of technologies on a project-wide basis to also be made aware of the potential benefits of electronic commerce. The promotion of technology partnerships could be used to foster closer integration within the supply chain.

Using alliances and partnerships - an industry approach

Present

■ Alliance/partnership driven by customer demand - marriage made by the customer (reactive).

■ Loose, informal alliance/partnership - driven by a response to a particular project (reactive).

Future

■ Fixed/permanent alliance - offered and promoted in a particular market place (proactive), i.e. offering a branded product.

■ Financially led alliance- alliance set up to offer one-stop shop to customers from inception to facilities management (proactive), i.e. PFI, BOT, DBFO.

Partnering/technology partnerships

Where trading partners keep each other at arm's length, uncertainty is maximized. As organizations come to manage their entire supply or value chains in a more proactive fashion, relationships are strengthened between key partners who may then become more willing and able to share information. This approach will ultimately result in a reduction in the number of basic exchanges, such as orders, between organizations.

Partnering, which can be practiced through the use of a set of strategic actions, can deliver vast improvements in construction performance and benefits to all partners involved. It is driven by partners who have a clear understanding of mutual objectives and a commitment to cooperative decision making and are all focused on using feedback to continuously improve their joint performance.

The Reading Construction Forum's 1998 report *The seven pillars of partnering* explains how seven elements form a controlled system for partnering that can deal with the rapidly changing markets and technologies that are shaping today's construction industry. The seven pillars are:

■ strategy - developing the client's objectives and how consultants, contractors and specialists can meet them on the basis of feedback

■ membership - identifying the firms that need to be involved to ensure all necessary skills are developed and available

■ equity - ensuring everyone is rewarded for their work on the basis of fair prices and fair profits

■ integration - improving the way the firms involved work together by using cooperation and building trust.

■ benchmarks - setting measured targets that lead to continuous improvements in performance from project to project

■ project processes - establishing standards and procedures that embody best practice based on process engineering

■ feedback - capturing lessons for projects and task forces to guide the development of strategy.

The increasing use of organizations for multiple projects (based on the development of long-term relationships between organizations) has alleviated the problem of how to encourage manufacturers and suppliers to invest in the hardware and software required for electronic commerce. Instead of competing for individual tenders, suppliers can establish a partnership with contractors, allowing them to develop electronic commerce solutions that extend beyond the life of a single project. This represents a shift away from project-based procurement of materials and components in favour of global agreements with suppliers guaranteeing long-term sourcing. Traditionally, UK construction companies have selected suppliers on the basis of lowest price, resulting in highly transient relationships with a large number of organizations. Partnership may therefore be a key element of a strategy designed to promote efficiency by fostering an environment for exploiting the wider benefits of information technology.

Stanhope-Bovis moving forward

Stanhope and Bovis are working together to achieve a culture of improvement in a quest for more efficient construction. At the heart of this culture of continuous improvement is a twelve-point improvement plan. Designated "Moving Forward", it aims to streamline the construction process while developing strong team relationships. The 'moving forward' initiatives that have been successfully implemented on six major projects include:

■ productivity

■ process mapping

■ material scheduling and control

■ waste management

■ prefabrication, preassembly and modularization

■ standardization

■ contractor initiative plans

■ skills and safety training

■ benchmarking

■ failure mode effect analysis

■ construction IT

■ delivery of design and procurement programmes.

Stanhope and Bovis have outlined the benefits they expect to gain from these initiatives. They range from improved worker motivation and team morale to continual improvement in cost, quality, time and certainty.

Chapter 5

Shaping people and tomorrow's construction organizations

There have been many prophecies about the rise and fall of companies in the future. Figure 14 shows what has actually happened to the construction industry as a whole during the 1970s, 1980s and 1990s.

The challenges

There are many challenges facing organizations in the construction sector. Some of the major ones are:

- low profitability of the contracting sector - housebuilding, materials and components supply and property investment companies show much better returns for their shareholders

- the short-term approach adopted by the City towards investment in construction

- low barriers for entry into the UK market by overseas firms

- construction is not seen as an attractive career for bright young people

- low capitalization of major UK construction organizations - there are no construction groups in the FTSE 100

- the lack of a strong capital base for consultants restricts their investment in new technology.

These challenges are not unique to the UK construction industry, many countries around the world have the same problems. There is no magic formula for producing higher profits – construction costs are too high relative to other goods and customers want lower construction costs and the benefits of a more efficient process. More realistic profits will not come from charging higher prices, they will come from driving out unnecessary costs, reducing waste and from making the design and construction process more efficient.

Profits will remain low while construction is seen as a low-technology industry and while too many firms are prepared to win work with low-profit margins. By using technology and engaging in lean design and lean thinking, waste can be eliminated and the process be made more efficient.

An inclusive approach to business

Construction organizations and consultancies will exist in the future, but they will be

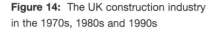

Figure 14: The UK construction industry in the 1970s, 1980s and 1990s

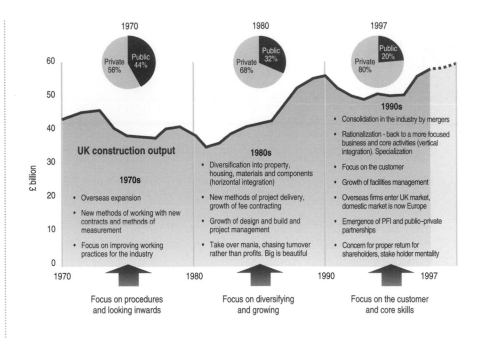

different to today's. The RSA's report *Tomorrow's company: the role of business in a changing world* has some significant messages for construction, which can be summarized as follows.

People and relationships are the key to sustainable success. The traditional view that companies exist solely to deliver profits to shareholders is being challenged. Companies are being urged to take an 'inclusive approach' to business, which involves altering the adversarial attitudes that traditionally characterize relationships between companies in the construction supply chain; reducing companies' dependence on purely financial measures of success and encouraging directors to broaden their understanding of legal responsibility, thus embracing a 'stakeholder' philosophy.

A stakeholder philosophy involves relationships between:

- suppliers
- customers
- employees
- local communities
- shareholders

with the vision for:

- partnership
- teamwork
- shared values
- shared goals
- shifting the emphasis from shareholders to stakeholders.

For many business leaders this is a familiar concept. The John Lewis Partnership is perhaps the ultimate example of a stakeholder company, where employees are partners. However there are sceptics, and some businesses leaders argue that, motivation apart, businesses do not have the knowledge to advance the public interest directly, and will serve their fellows best if they concentrate on maximizing their shareholders' equity rather than on promoting exports, combating global warming or solving community issues.

However, the case for change is clear and the construction sector has to overcome its complacency and develop the positive attitude required to meet the challenges.

Low profitability

The Fortune 500[1] ratings (1998) make interesting reading for the construction industry.

- Ten engineering and construction companies appear in the Fortune 500, of those two are French, one is American and seven are Japanese.

- Pharmaceuticals is the best industry, with a median return on revenue of 17.2%, trading is the worst industry on 0.2% with engineering and construction only one place higher on 0.8%.

- Engineering and construction remains on 0.8% for the median return on assets. Banks take last place with 0.3% while pharmaceuticals again lead with 14.9%.

- Engineering and construction is in eighth place for assets per employee, at £0.6 million.

- Over the past five years the median return for engineering and construction revenue has not been above 1%.

Commentators have been forecasting the demise of the general contractor and the demise of consultants in their current form. The barrier between consultants and contractors will disappear. The big corporate head offices will be slimmed down and there will be no boundaries between functions and professions, teamworking will be the basis of delivering what the customer wants.

Long-term employability will only be achieved by those who learn new skills. Full-time work is on the decrease, in 1994 around 60% of employment was full-time but the numbers of temporary and part-time workers is increasing. Service providers, who outsource to specialist providers, are growing in importance.

Ethical issues are high on the list of customers' priorities. There is an increasing need for companies to maintain the confidence of the public in the legitimacy of their operations and business conduct - they need a 'licence to operate.' One approach to achieving confidence is through development of community relationships by increasingly participating in national and local community partnerships

Tomorrow's construction organization

Construction organizations have to change to meet the challenges ahead. To this end, this report advocates:

- customer focus

- greater integration in the supply chain

- more transparency between design and production

- better use of enabling technology for process improvement.

So what will happen to the construction organization? A range of experts have put forward the following suggestions.

- There will be a small number of mega-players in design and construction, with a large number of small service providers.

- A number of global construction organizations will emerge, who will have the financial muscle to take risks and to invest in research and development.

---

1 *Fortune 500* lists the top 500 companies world-wide across 31 industry sectors.

- There will be more involvement of overseas firms in the UK market, whether it be in the manufacture and supply of components or in construction. The global market place means that firms will bring a new culture and value system. The domestic market will be Europe.

- There will be more specialization in companies, with brand image becoming increasingly important, for instance some firms will specialize exclusively in healthcare projects, others in education or retailing.

- The boundary between consultant and contractor will become blurred and there will be considerable overlap in the service offered by both sectors. The focus will be on delivery of the product.

- Equity stakes in large projects will become the usual practice to secure work. Small and medium-sized firms will become part of consortia for projects where the risk is shared.

- Non price-led tenders will be based on the level of service, project guarantees and whole-life appraisal.

- There will be fewer regional offices, companies will use technology to integrate their office functions.

- The departmental structure of companies, currently based upon functions (such as estimating, planning, purchasing/buying, legal services), will disappear and be replaced by integrated teams in-house and by outsourced services. Information technology services will be provided by specialist companies.

- Specialization will be the order of the day, the 'general provider' will still operate but only on small projects.

- The big materials suppliers and components manufacturers will exert a major influence on design and installation through their technology and buying power. They have the ability to introduce lean supply and lean design. It has already happened in some sectors.

- Alliances (strategic and group) will grow in importance, with many alliances being with companies from outside the construction industry.

- Project creation teams which are alert to project financing will become increasingly important.

- Companies will be linked electronically, creating seamless integration.

- Understanding logistics and supply-chain management will be a core part of the service providers' business.

- Organizations will manage risk as a process rather than monitoring it.

- Merchanting of materials will do for construction what logistics has done for food retailing.

- Franchising could happen in the construction industry.

Tomorrow's company: the ground rules

- Tomorrow's company must focus on stakeholders and stakeholder relationships. The conventional wisdom is to define the business in terms of immediate financial performance and returns to shareholders: other participants are seen merely as a means to an end. Only through deepened relationships with and between employees, customers, suppliers, investors and the community will companies anticipate, innovate and adapt fast enough.

- There must be a focus on learning from all those who contribute to the business by building upon reciprocal relationships with customers, suppliers and other key stakeholders - a partnership approach.

- The company must understand and anticipate the needs of the customer's customer and respond accordingly. "We must make what we can sell and not try to sell what we make."

- Yesterday's companies see customers as a source of revenue and profit and sales as transactions - they compete on price. Tomorrow's company needs to add value for customers and seek demanding customers who will drive innovation and competitiveness.

- Yesterday's companies regard suppliers as interchangeable vendors, they see cost cutting as a zero sum game by which profits are increased only at the expense of suppliers. Tomorrow's company must view key suppliers as an extension of the company. It must set targets and pursue them jointly with suppliers, sharing information and new ideas.

- Companies which want to prosper will have to be fast on their feet, good learners, capable of inspiring loyalty and superb with their relationships with their people, suppliers and customers.

- Lifetime employment can no longer be assured. The old idea of the employer and employee will become obsolete - no one can feel secure.

- Tomorrow's construction company must have a commitment to innovation throughout the whole organization.

Recognize that the pace of change will quicken. Of the eleven companies named between 1979 and 1989 by Management Today *as Britain's most profitable company, four subsequently collapsed and two were acquired.*

Figure 15 brings together all the enabling technologies that have been discussed in this report. It shows how the various data capture, data manipulation and data transfer technologies can be integrated into a coherent IT strategy.

Figure 15: Using technology to integrate the construction process

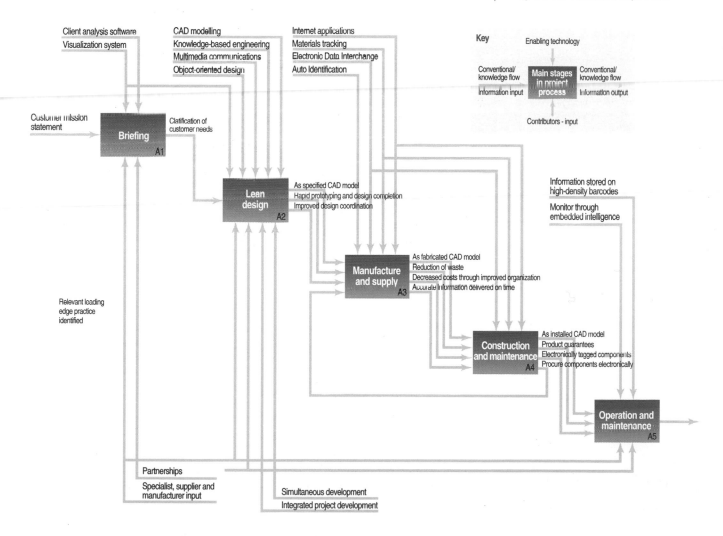

The big issues

All the above ground rules must be viewed within the context of the external pressures that organizations will face. The big issues that will affect the business climate are:

- environmental pressures
- sustainability
- safety of the workforce
- ethics
- stakeholder philosophy.

People issues within technological and process change

The technological and process improvements presented in this report imply changes to working patterns. The technologies give organizations the ability to deliver what customers want. If people are made aware that technologies are not job-threatening they will be more willing to use them.

Resistance to change

The resistance of organizations and their members to change is one of the most well-documented findings from studies of individual and organizational behaviour. Factors that cause resistance to change include:

- the widespread misunderstanding of technology
- attitudes of staff to new technology
- the reluctance of organizations and people to embrace a technology which appears complicated
- fear of unknown changes or uncertainty - people resist something they cannot predict or understand
- desire not to lose something of value - where technology is perceived as a threat to them or the system that they value
- fear of inability to handle new requirements - people resist technology if they feel unable or inadequate to handle associated requirements
- inadequate understanding of the need to change - people resist technology if they feel that the costs outweigh the benefits
- poor implementation efforts - inadequate planning, user involvement and insufficient training
- labour/management relations - a lack of mutual trust and openness between labour and management.

All the recommendations in this report (both technology and process based) have been implemented extensively within other industrial sectors. However, there is an education and training requirement. Overcoming human barriers to change will play a key role in securing eventual acceptance.

Overcoming resistance

When developing a strategy to avoid any resistance to implementation of change, it is necessary to address the issues of:

- education and training
- participation and involvement

- negotiation and agreement - offering incentives is another way of avoiding potential resistance and is particularly effective where it is clear that a party stands to lose as a result of the change

- explicit and implicit coercion - managers may force people to accept the introduction of technology by explicitly or implicitly threatening them or by transferring them.

Education

The education and the involvement with all those in the supply chain is essential to an integrated process. Knowledge of the needs and problems faced by other parties in the chain must be fully understood if mutual benefits are to be achieved. Continued IT education is essential throughout the construction industry to ensure that all those interfacing with enabling technologies have the necessary skills.

Meeting the demands of tomorrow

Today's organizations need to identify and implement changes to meet the demands of tomorrow's global competition. People and relationships are the key to sustainable success. Tomorrow's successful company will have bridged the gaps between the players and the process by adopting a holistic approach. Its money will have been diverted from defensive behaviour and contractual disputes to involvement in success factors such as training, continuous improvement, and research and development.

Imagine

Q. As a small plumbing and heating company - how can new technology help me?

A. Nowadays a lot of time is spent searching for materials. Imagine:

- being able to look at the plumbers' merchant's stock list on a computer located at your office

- ordering the stock without going to the merchant's yard

- ordering the stock and seeing the invoice total on the screen (imagine the benefits when preparing a bid)

- the merchant's expert system being able to profile your use and bringing up your most regularly used items on the screen

- having a computer screen that you touch, rather than having to type in data

- having a pump that has an electronic tag embedded in it which told you on a hand-held reader what is wrong with the pump and the part number to be used for ordering a replacement.

All these activities are currently in use, it is a small step to implementation.

Chapter 6
The next stage

Preparing for the future: steps to change

This report has proposed a number of key activities that organizations should be considering to achieve a lean process.

- Improve customer focus - how can customers' needs can be better understood and how can firms respond and adapt to meet these needs?

- Focus on developing a joint approach - what needs to be done to improve integration between all parties in the construction process, and how can organizations improve the performance of their specialists and suppliers.

- Process improvement - eliminate non value-adding processes and make remaining activities more efficient.

- Use technology to support and improve the process - how will IT and electronic commerce affect firms and the way they do business, and what will the effects be on customers and suppliers? How can competitive advantage be achieved by introducing intelligence into products?

There are a number of steps that can be taken now as part of a process of implementation of the principles advocated in this report.

Four steps to achieving lean design

1. Focus on design

- Develop the use of standard components and standard design solutions

- Do not start designs from scratch every time.

- Use object modelling and knowledge-based engineering to develop standard objects that can be reused across designs.

- Make communications a priority.

2. Maintain customer focus

- Focus on customer needs and not the needs of the construction industry.

- Use design visualization to help customers gain confidence in the design team.

- Work in partnership, rather than as an adversary.

- Exclude the exclusions.

A cynic's view

Question: I have lived through modular coordination and endless proposals to standardize design details and to use off-the-shelf standard components. None of these have been successful in the past so why should they work now?

Answer: The reasons are customer power and spiralling construction costs. User-friendly CAD has allowed standardization of design to be a reality. Customers are now demanding change towards standardization.

- Avoid surprises for the client.

- Take a whole-life approach to the project.

- Manage and avoid risk, do not simply monitor it.

- Use IT to capture and store clients' requirements.

- Focus on the man-machine interface, use touch screens and voice transmission wherever feasible.

3. Eliminate non value-adding processes

- Design with production processes in mind. Do not pay lip service to buildability - make it part of the design process.

- Focus on planning to eliminate unnecessary design iterations and reworking of designs.

- Work closely with supply chain partners to identify non value-adding activities.

- Ensure specialist input at the early stages of design.

4. Focus on the supply chain

- Work closely with selected supply chain partners to make remaining value-adding steps more efficient.

- Invest jointly in the implementation of technologies to develop CAD modelling facilities.

- Consider how working concurrently can improve development times.

Three steps to achieving lean supply

1. Process improvement

- Develop use of standard components and standard design solutions.

- Do not start designs from scratch every time.

- Use object modelling and knowledge-based engineering to develop standard objects that can be reused in new designs.

2. Use technology to support the reengineered process

- Apply automated materials management and inventory control systems.

- Eliminate manual data capture and entry by ensuring that materials are electronically tagged.

- Streamline re-engineered processes by allowing the electronic transmission of trading data and project data.

- Invest in joint research and development initiatives with all suppliers.

- Support all suppliers in the implementation and application of data management techniques.

- Develop joint procedures for evaluation of technology and ensure that all suppliers share in the benefits.

3. Managing supplier relationships

- Create a stable base with fewer suppliers - to enable the build up of trust, economies of scale and, through continuity in the relationship, implementation of process and technology change.

- Create alliances with organizations with continuous improvement strategies and with similar long-term views and technological competencies.

- Use technology clusters to integrate systems with specialists and suppliers.

- Establish a clear understanding of the scope of change together with expectations and deliverables sought - joint scoping.

- Ensure paths and procedures for dispute resolution are in place.

- Arrange regular reviews of the performance of suppliers.

- Set mutual objectives and the metrics for measuring improvement.

A vision of what a construction project could look like in the next century, if the recommendations of this report are implemented, is presented by Project 2010. All aspects of Project 2010 are available for immediate use by organizations and, in many cases use tried and tested technologies and techniques. Project 2010 embraces change that is applicable to small, medium and large firms alike. The construction industry needs firm and practical examples of success before any advances will be embraced, it is therefore proposed that demonstration projects be set up as recommended in the Construction Task Force Report of 1998.

When change can be shown to bring benefits, people and organizations do respond - look what happened in the 1980s with the growth of fee contracting on major projects and for facilities management.

Designers should consider:

- closer integration of design and construction, involving suppliers and manufacturers

- design that is fit for purpose on a whole-life basis

- customization of standard design solutions to meet customer requirements

- the extent to which the brief represents the total sum of the customer's requirements

- involving suppliers, manufacturers and specialists in the design process

- using bespoke designs only in response to explicit customer requirements.

Construction organizations should consider:

- committing everybody in the organization to achieving customer satisfaction

- thinking beyond the sale

- ensuring that designers, suppliers and manufacturers all understand what customers want

- providing more formalized feedback to designers and manufacturers about customer issues.

Project 2010: A vision of construction in the year 2010

Customer focus

■ The construction service provider is appointed at the business case stage and works in collaboration with the integrated project design team.

■ The customer is involved throughout the design process as a member of the project community and uses virtual reality walk-through of the project as it evolves.

■ All parties to the design process have a strong focus on production and delivery to time and cost.

■ The project is guaranteed with zero defects and there is a five-year guarantee against defects in workmanship and materials offered by the constructor.

■ Culture is based on trust and respect. Priorities for the people are ensuring the customers' needs are met.

Integrated design and construction

■ Partnerships are more widespread in 2010 - these allow construction companies to spread the cost of investing in enabling technologies and allow continuous improvement in supply chain management.

■ All members of the team use an integrated project design system with common CAD and management information systems. Extensive use in the design system is made of object-oriented design and knowledge-based engineering systems.

■ Materials manufacturers, components manufacturers and suppliers are linked to the design team's CAD system. They provide comprehensive information, which is transmitted electronically to the CAD system. The relationship with the materials manufacturers and suppliers is based on a long-term agreed partnership.

■ Throughout design, a computer builds an electronic prototype of the project to ensure optimization of all resources. All members of design and production are involved in evaluating the project prototype.

■ Design is 90% complete and agreed prior to any production taking place, even where design and construction are overlapped.

■ Franchising is widely used in construction. Many of the major suppliers on the project are franchises of major global companies which provide product guarantees on quality of performance. Advanced orders to preferred suppliers are placed via the integrated design system.

■ On site, the workforce has access to touch-screen technology with computer terminals located around the site. All information on the project will be stored in a database that will be accessed either by voice on touch screen technology. The fear of computers will disappear.

■ Materials and components are selected on the basis of having embedded intelligence which can be used at the facilities management stage. Relevant information is stored on a high-density barcode or on an electronic tag.

■ Electronic Data Interchange is used for transferring orders, invoices, delivery notes and payment between contractors, suppliers and manufacturers.

■ All materials and components on site are barcoded to improve materials management. Intelligent tags provide all information on storage, fixing, health and safety, operation, maintenance and disposal of materials.

■ Materials delivery is tracked via geographic information systems, with an up-date on progress. On receipt at the site it will be registered by scanning intelligent tags and payment will be automatically triggered electronically.

Regulation and approval

■ Outline and detailed planning approvals are granted after the planning committee has experienced a virtual reality walk-through of the project showing its impact on the surrounding environment and traffic systems.

■ Building regulations approvals are granted electronically using the integrated CAD system which interfaces with the granting authority's knowledge-based engineering system.

■ An environmental impact check is undertaken by a program which ensures compliance. An environmental compliance certificate is issued electronically.

Facilities management

■ The customer is given an electronic CAD 3-D model of the building which can be used for facilities management and gives 'as built' information.

Cost planning and monitoring

■ Cost is monitored throughout the design stage using an expert system. The bid is generated automatically and negotiation takes place on the profit margin and overhead allowance. A cost guarantee is offered to the customer.

■ Customers pay on agreed stages of completion and payment is transmitted electronically.

Bibliography and references

Baldwin A N, Thorpe A & Alkaabi J A, 1994, Improved materials management through bar-coding: results and implications from a feasibility study, *Civil Engineering*, **102**, Nov., 156-162.

Banwell, Sir H, 1964, *The Placing and Management of Contracts for Building and Civil Engineering work*, HMSO.

Bennett J & Jayes S, 1995, *Trusting the Team: the best practice guide to partnering in construction*, Centre for Strategic Studies in Construction.

Bennett, J & Jayes S, 1998, *The Seven Pillars of Partnering: A guide to second generation partnering*, Reading Construction Forum.

Bennett J, Pothecary E P & Robinson G D, 1996, *Designing and Building a world-class industry*, Centre for Strategic Studies in Construction.

British Property Federation, 1983, *Manual of the British Property Federation System for building design and construction*, British Property Federation.

Construction Industry Board, 1997, *Briefing the Team, a guide to better briefing for clients*, Thomas Telford Publishing.

Construction Industry Board, 1997, *Partnering in the Team*, Thomas Telford Publishing.

Construct IT Centre of Excellence, 1997, *The Armathwaite Initiative, Global Construction IT Futures International Meeting*, Construct IT Centre of Excellence.

Construction Clients' Forum, 1998, *Constructing Improvement*, Construction Customers' Forum

Construction Task Force Report, 1998, *Rethinking Construction*, DETR

Davis, S and Botkin, J, 1994, *Harvard Busness Review*.

Emmerson Sir H, 1956, The Ministry of Works, George Allen & Unwin Ltd.

Emmerson Sir H, 1962, *Survey of Problems Before the Construction Industries*, Report prepared for the Ministry of Works, HMSO.

Fisher N, Barlow R, Garnett N, Finch E, Newcombe R, 1997, *Project modelling in construction ...seeing is believing*, Thomas Telford Publishing.

Gray C, Hughes W & Bennett J, 1994, *The successful management of design, A handbook of building design management*, Centre for Strategic Studies in Construction

Gray C, 1996, *Value for Money: Helping the UK afford the buildings it likes*, Reading Construction Forum

Higgin G & Jessop N, 1963, *Communications in the Building Industry*. A Pilot Study Commissioned by The National Joint Consultative Committee of Architects, Quantity Surveyors and Builders, Tavistock Institute of Human Relations.

Jones M & Saad M, 1998, *Unlocking Specialist Potential: A more participative role for specialist contractors*, Reading Construction Forum

Latham Sir M, 1994, *Constructing The Team, Final Report of the Government/Industry Review of Procurement and Contractual Arrangements in the UK Industry*, HMSO.

Lamming R, 1993, *Beyond Partnership: Strategies for Innovation and Lean Supply*, Prentice Hall.

Marsh L, Flanagan R & Finch E, 1997, *Enabling Technologies: a primer on barcoding for construction*, CIOB

National Economic Development Office, 1967, *Action on the Banwell Report*, HMSO

National Economic Development Office, 1975, *The Professions and their Role in Improving the Performance of the Construction Industries - A Feasibility Study*

Royal Institute of British Architects, 1967, *Plan of work*, RIBA

RSA, 1997, *Tomorrow's Company*, Gower

Report of the Central Council of Works and Buildings, HMSO

Royal Institution of Chartered Surveyors, 1998, *The Challenge of Change*, RICS

Simon, E D, 1944, *The Placing and Management of Building Contracts*.

Suchocki M, 1998, *The Genesis Project - a manufacturing approach for construction*, CIRIA, Project Report 5.

Tavistock Institute, 1966, *Interdependence and Uncertainty. A Study of the Building Industry*, Tavistock Publications.

Technology Foresight, 1995, *Technology Foresight Reports 1-16, Progress Through Partnership*, HMSO.

Thorpe A, Baldwin B, Carter C, Leevers D & Madigan D, 1995, Multimedia communications in construction, *Civil Engineering*, **108**, Feb., 12-16

UK construction Challenge, 1990, *Can the UK reduce its construction costs without affecting quality?* Lynton plc.

United Kingdom Offshore Operators Association, 1994, *CRINE Cost Reduction initiative For the New ERA*, The Insitute of Petrolium.

University of Reading, 1988, *Building Britain 2001*, Centre for Strategic Studies in Construction.

Womack J P, Jones D T & Roos D, 1990, *The Machine That Changed the World*, Rawson Associates.

Womack J P & Jones D T, 1996, *Lean Thinking, Banish waste and create wealth in your corporation*, Simon & Schuster.

The Reading Construction Forum

The Reading Construction Forum is a group of major UK customers, contractors, consultants, manufacturers and stakeholders located at the University of Reading. It has close links with the Department of Construction Management & Engineering but is independent of the University and regularly commissions research from other universities.

Members of the Forum are major companies concerned with improving the satisfaction and profitability of construction industry customers both occasional and experienced and both large and small. All are committed to working together to achieve change and innovation in the British and European building industries.

To achieve effective change the Forum is led by its Principal Members who are drawn from international customers and building industry consultants, contractors and manufacturers. They work with leading researchers to identify specific actions needed to improve the performance of the UK building industry.

"The over-riding purpose of the Forum is to enlist the active involvement of members in identifying and implementing best practice."

The objectives are designed to achieve change by collaborative involvement rather than by perpetuating the confrontational aspects of the industry that historically have damaged its performance. To these ends the objectives of the Forum are:

- to provide a forum for members about all issues affecting quality, efficiency and innovation in the design, construction and use of commercial and industrial buildings
- to identify the need for specific changes
- to ensure that good practice which unites the industry in the interests of customers is widely disseminated
- to encourage the research and development needed to ensure that the changes are effective and beneficial
- to take practical actions at improving the international competitiveness of the building industries of Britain and Europe, including helping to improve relationships between industry and Government
- to implement the results of research by the Reading Construction Forum
- to work closely with other organizations committed to changing the construction industry for the better.

The Forum consists of the following companies:

Principal members

Bovis Europe	O'Rourke Group
Building Design Partnership	Richard Rogers Partnership
Roger Bullivant Ltd	ROM Limited
Drake & Scull Engineering Ltd	Sainsbury plc
Gardiner & Theobald	Slough Estates plc
John Laing plc	Stanhope Plc
John Lewis Partnership	Tarmac

Ordinary members

Andover Controls Ltd	Land Securities Plc
Barclays Property Holdings	Mansell
Birse Construction Ltd	John Mowlem Construction Plc
B & Q Plc	Nabarro Nathanson
British Gypsum Ltd	Otis plc
Bucknall Group	R G Construction Management
Coverite Ltd	Shepherd Construction Ltd
Galliford (UK) Ltd	SmithKline Beecham
Gleeds	Stent Foundations
M J Gleeson Group Plc	Taylor Joynson Garrett
Ernest Green & Parts Holdings Plc	Tesco Stores Ltd
Hochtief	Try Construction Ltd
Irvine Whitlock Ltd	Union Railways Ltd
Kyle Stewart	Wates Integra

Other Forum reports

Trusting the Team

The best-practice guide to partnering in construction, by John Bennett and Sarah Jayes of the University of Reading, with the 'Partnering' task force of the Reading Construction Forum, chaired by Charles Johnston of Sainsbury's.

Value for Money

Helping the UK afford the buildings it likes, by Colin Gray of the University of Reading, with the 'Value for Money' task force of the Reading Construction Forum, chaired by Dr Bernard Rimmer of Slough Estates plc.

The Seven Pillars of Partnering

A guide to second generation partnering by John Bennett and Sarah Jayes of the University of Reading, with the 'Partnering' task force of the Reading Construction Forum, chaired by Charles Johnston of Sainsbury's.

Unlocking Specialist Potential

A more participative role for specialist contractors, by Dr Mohammed Saad and Martyn Jones of the University of West England, with the 'Specialist Contractors' task force of the Reading Construction Forum, chaired by Martin Davis of Drake & Scull Engineering.

For further details on these publications please contact:

Reading Construction Forum, The University of Reading

PO Box 219, Whiteknights, Reading RG6 6AW

Telephone 0118 931 8766

Fax 0118 931 3856

email m.p.dodds@reading.ac.uk

Learning Resources
Centre